HAMLYN BIRD BEHAVIOUR GUIDES

BIRDS OF PREY

HAMLYN BIRD BEHAVIOUR GUIDES

BIRDS OF PREY

NICHOLAS HAMMOND
BRUCE PEARSON

HAMLYN

TITLE PAGE ILLUSTRATION *A Short-toed Eagle, having killed a large snake on the ground, takes to the air.*

First published in 1993 by Hamlyn,
an imprint of Reed Consumer Books,
Michelin House, 81 Fulham Road, London SW3 6RB

Text © Nicholas Hammond 1993
Illustrations © Bruce Pearson 1993
Map © Reed Consumer Books 1993

British Library Cataloguing in Publication Data

Hammond, Nicholas
  Birds of Prey. – (Hamlyn Bird
  Behaviour Guides)
  I. Title II. Pearson, Bruce III. Series
  598.9

ISBN 0-540-01277-7

Page design by Jessica Caws
Map by Louise Griffiths

Printed in Hong Kong

ACKNOWLEDGEMENTS
The authors would like to thank Richard Porter for looking at and suggesting improvements to the pictures, David Christie for copy editing the text, and Jo Hemmings and the editorial and design staff for their enthusiasm and creativity.

CONTENTS

INTRODUCTION

Inevitably, the first question that any birdwatcher asks when faced with a bird is: 'What species it it?' But how many go on to the next question: 'What's it doing?' In some cases the answer to the second question may give the birdwatcher an important clue to the bird's identity. Although understanding what the bird is doing may not always be diagnostic in its identification, it will certainly help build up a picture of the bird and its habits.

This book covers all of the Accipitriformes, Pandioniformes and Falconiformes likely to be encountered in the zoogeographical region known as the Western Palearctic. This area covers Europe south from the Arctic, and North Africa to the northern limit of the Sahel; from the western boundary from Iceland and the Azores, it extends to the Urals and the western frontier of Iran (see map on pages 124-5).

The Accipitriformes, Pandioniformes and Falconiformes might be described as 'diurnal birds of prey' to distinguish them from the owls (Strigiformes), most of which are nocturnal. The definition 'birds of prey' is used by some birdwatchers to cover all four orders, but it ignores the fact that any bird which eats other animals is in effect a bird of prey. To distinguish owls from other birds of prey the prefix 'nocturnal' is used for owls and 'diurnal' for the others, but this, too, is unsatisfactory, because some species of owl hunt in daylight.

The word 'raptor' is a shorter alternative to 'diurnal bird of prey' and will be used throughout this book. It is still not satisfactorily definitive, because it derives from the Latin word meaning 'snatcher', and while this is an adequate description of all the species covered here with the exception of the vultures, we shall gloss over the fact that it might equally be applied to the owls.

Fifty-three species of raptor have been recorded in the Western Palearctic. Of these, nine do not breed in the area and are only rare vagrants. We have, therefore, concentrated on those species that are regular breeders. Rather than arrange this book by individual species we have grouped the species by behaviour. Thus, those species that hunt in flocks are grouped together in the co-operative hunting section of the chapter on feeding behaviour, but each also occurs in other chapters, which cover breeding behaviour and migration.

The chapter on breeding behaviour covers the various strategies adopted by different species and how knowledge of the breeding behaviour of species can help in field identification. Display flights are an obvious example of this.

A Lesser Spotted Eagle hunts small mammals by quartering a newly mown hayfield in the Biebrza Valley, an important bird area in eastern Poland

The behaviour of birds may vary with their development, and raptors often take several years to reach maturity. Immature birds may be difficult to identify and the adult plumages of some species may be very variable between individuals, but looking at their behaviour may help to confirm identification.

Because of the migratory behaviour of many species of raptor it is possible to pinpoint locations where they can be seen with some certainty. Other species can be found by understanding their habitat requirements. The gazetteer on pages 126–153 covers sites from which to watch migration, and areas where raptors can be seen at other times of year.

FEEDING

Raptors are flesh-eaters. They catch their prey with their feet and tear the flesh with their hooked bills. Within these generalizations different species have undergone various physical and behavioural adaptations to help them make the most of the food available in their environments.

ADAPTATIONS FOR FEEDING

The amount of specialization varies among species, but each has adapted to enable it to deal most effectively with the sizes and types of animal on which it preys. For example, the White-tailed Eagle has huge feet with powerful talons for catching birds up to the size of Whooper Swans, and a large, heavy bill for tearing into the flesh of this comparatively large prey. By contrast, the Honey Buzzard, which catches insects in its bill, has barely curved talons which become worn as it digs out the nests of wasps and bees; a specialist in eating these, and the contents of their nests, it also has a relatively small bill and is protected from stings by the dense feathering of its face.

Europe's most specialized bird of prey is the Osprey, which feeds almost entirely on freshly caught fish. Herons, terns, kingfishers and most fish-eating birds catch their prey in their bills, but the Osprey, in common with other fishing raptors, uses its feet. These relatively large feet have toes of equal length with long, fine-pointed curved claws, and tiny spikelets 1 mm long on the soles of the feet to secure slippery fish. The outer toe is also reversible, which enables the bird to hold its prey with two toes pointing forward and two pointing aft. Its fine bill is sharp enough to tear through the scales of fish. Its nostrils are in the form of slits which close on impact with the water.

Flight adaptations

The shape of raptors in flight provides significant pointers to their behaviour. The length and shape of tail, wings and legs are adapted to the most effective hunting techniques: the long, pointed wings of falcons give them speed, but even among similarly sized species there are visible differences. The differences in the hunting techniques of the Peregrine and the Eleonora's Falcon have led to differences in shape. The Peregrine displays a mastery of speed, but while it can

By hovering head-to-wind with tail fanned and rapidly quivering wingtips, the Kestrel is able to hold its head steady to see as clearly as possible its prey of small mammals, lizards or large insects on the ground.

indulge in dramatic aerobatics it has less need of aerial agility than the Eleonora's Falcon. The Peregrine stoops on its prey from a great height, relying on speed to kill: it does not need suddenly to change direction, while the Eleonora's Falcon hunts flying insects when there are no small migrant birds available. The comparatively longer tail of the Eleonora's Falcon acts as both a balance and a rudder, allowing the falcon to twist in pursuit of its insect prey.

A long tail also gives the bird added braking power and allows it to fly more slowly. By spreading their long tails, kites and harriers can fly very slowly in their search for prey. It is an advantage for the raptor when hunting prey on the ground to be as stationary as possible, so that it can scan the ground thoroughly. For example, the hunting Kestrel remains in the same position by hovering with wingtips quivering very fast and tail spread to act as both brake and rudder to hold it head-to-wind. Sparrowhawks hunt small birds in wooded country and along hedges, relying on surprise. They do not need sustained speed, but they must be able to twist and turn through twigs and branches. Their wings are short in comparison to those of the similarly sized Kestrel, but their long tails allow them the agility to chase highly mobile smaller birds in close country.

In the open a small bird is no match for a Kestrel, but if that bird can successfully reach cover the odds in its favour improve. On a winter's day I watched a female Kestrel chase a Greenfinch into a large willow. The Greenfinch made for the centre of the tree, where the Kestrel was unable to catch it, because her long wings made her movement through the twiggy branches much slower than that of the smaller, more agile prey. Nevertheless, she approached close enough to her intended victim to make it uncomfortable. Had the finch stayed in the tree it might have succeeded in escaping the talons of the Kestrel, but it made a dash for freedom: it flew about 25 m from the tree to some long grass on a river bank. At first it seemed that the Kestrel would not press home her attack, but after several seconds she dashed from the tree in a long, fast swoop which ended in the Greenfinch being caught on the ground as if it were a vole. Although Kestrels and other falcons can spread their wings and soar, they do so less readily than the broad-winged eagles and vultures.

The Golden Eagle hunts over a very wide area in search of prey. To minimize the amount of energy used in travelling the eagle soars on its long wings, which are 'fingered' to allow it to fly without stalling.

The birds best adapted for soaring are the massive albatrosses of the southern oceans, the largest of which has narrow wings up to 3.5 m long. Such long wings present few problems for birds that nest on the ground in open country and spend most of their lives at sea, but for a Golden Eagle living in the mountains, nesting on a cliff edge and catching jinking prey on the ground such long wings would be too cumbersome, presenting a major problem to the way of life of a raptor. The eagle's long wings with 'fingered' wingtips are, therefore, a compromise allowing it to manoeuvre near to the ground in close pursuit of its prey. The primaries at the wingtip have notches, known as emarginations, on both sides, giving each feather a pointed tip. The effect is to create rectangular slots at the wingtip between each set of two adjacent feathers. These slots reduce turbulence at the extremities of the wing.

The emarginations on the tips of the wings of Griffon Vultures are even more marked than those on the wings of Golden Eagles. The vultures do not need the agility of eagles because the carrion on which they feed is motionless. Nor, therefore, do they need long tails to add to their manoeuvrability. In flight, their very short tails are rarely very noticeable, as the secondaries are long, which gives flying Griffons the appearance of a 'flying door'. These sail-like wings give them the ability to soar, remaining airborne on thermals for many hours and covering many kilometres in their search for food.

Another vulturine feature is the shagginess of their plumage. This seems to create friction that helps the birds to maintain a slow speed for greater efficiency in scanning the landscape for food. The antithesis of this is the tightly moulded plumage of the Peregrine which needs to be as aerodynamically efficient as possible to increase its speed when diving from a great height on to its prey.

Toes and talons

Feet are an important feature of raptors. It is with these that they snatch their prey. As previously mentioned, the Osprey has long, curved sharp claws and spiky soles with which to grasp slippery fish, but all species of raptor demonstrate, to a greater or lesser extent, features that help them to cope with their prey much more effectively. Rarely in the field does the birdwatcher have such a good view of a raptor that he or she has time to study its feet. Besides, it has always been my experience that when watching a perched bird of prey at close quarters one's attention is drawn more towards its eyes and its bill. However, a visit to a museum to study the feet of birds of prey is to be recommended: it can give point to what could otherwise be a rather depressing trip around the folly of a gun-toting member of the Victorian squirearchy.

Sparrowhawks and Hen Harriers have long, fine legs for reaching after prey, but the feet of each species are significantly different. Sparrowhawks have long toes with long, sharp talons and feet with a wide spread so that they can grasp agile prey. Harriers have comparatively shorter toes with less spread, because they take relatively small prey which they kill on the ground. Similarly, the Kestrel has shorter toes than the Sparrowhawk.

Stooping fast on flying birds, the Peregrine needs short legs and powerful feet, capable of killing and grasping its prey in flight. The Peregrine kills by hitting the prey at the base of the skull with its hind toe. The Eleonora's Falcon, which is of a similar size, relies less on surprise and sheer power and, because it feeds on smaller birds and insects caught in flight; its legs are comparatively longer and its feet more slender than those of the Peregrine.

Among the strongest-footed of birds of prey are the large eagles. The Golden Eagle's powerful foot can crush the life from a hare, as the front three claws squeeze the flesh against the large rear talon. Buzzards do share many features with the Golden Eagle, but these are moderated versions more suited to the Buzzard's less specialized way of life. Its foot, for example, is similar to that of an eagle, but comparatively smaller and more generalized, capable of dealing with prey ranging from earthworms and frogs to rabbits and partridges.

Vultures and Honey Buzzards have talons that are barely curved, because vultures have no need to kill their prey and Honey Buzzards kill their insect prey with their bills.

Bills and heads

Bills of raptors, like their feet, vary with the prey that they take. The fish-specialist Osprey, for example, has a sharp bill for tearing into the flesh of its prey, while the White-tailed Eagle has a massive bill with a sharp hook for coping with large fish, carcases of seals and large birds. Small prey calls for smaller bills. Harriers, which feed on small mammals and birds, have quite delicate bills, and the insect-eating Honey Buzzard's is comparatively straight. The Buzzard's bill, like its feet, is a smaller, more generalized version of the Golden Eagle's.

Most raptors kill by crushing the life from their prey with their feet. The more delicate-footed falcons may have to use their bills to give the *coup de grâce* to their prey and have a notch in the upper mandible against which the neck of the victim is held steady while it is dispatched by a quick bite to the back of the neck.

The heavy hooked bills of the larger vultures are adapted for tearing through the muscles and flesh of carrion, but the smaller Egyptian Vulture has a finer, curved bill, capable of dealing with a range of scavenged scraps and reaching the places that the other vultures' bills cannot reach. It is usually the last vulture to leave food and will pick over the ground in search of morsels. If it takes these morsels away it carries them in its bill, not in its claws. It has a wider range of food than the other vultures, using its bill to take insects, reptiles and amphibians.

Three of the five species of vulture that breed in the region have bare faces, which is in part an adaptation to feeding in the depths of a bloody carcase. The Griffon Vulture's head and neck are covered with down rather than with contour feathers, an adaptation which may be a means of avoiding the contour feathers becoming matted with blood.

HUNTING RANGES AND TERRITORIES

When birds have paired, competition for food or over mates distracts them from the serious business of breeding. To prevent this competition between birds of the same species, therefore, they hold territories from which all other individuals of the same species are excluded.

Three types of territory have been defined for raptors: the nesting area, the home range and the winter territory, all of which will be defended at some time against other members of the same species, against larger birds of prey and against crows.

Nesting territory is determined not only by the imperative need to maintain food supplies. It is also necessary to prevent sexual competition from unmated individuals or neighbours. The extent of the nesting territory may be a few metres for colonially nesting Griffon Vultures and less in the case of Lesser Kestrels. Peregrines will defend breeding territories with a radius of less than 1 km and will attack intruders outside this area, disputing over food and perches over a radius of a further 2 km. Golden Eagles in Scotland will maintain nesting territories of an average of 57 km^2. Maintaining a territory also helps to maintain the pair-bond, which is important for species with an incubation period of several weeks and where the male is needed to hunt food for the young.

The home range is more extensive than the nesting territory and is the area over which the breeding pair hunts. It may overlap with that of other breeding pairs. Ospreys maintain breeding territories, from which potential rivals are excluded, but share lakes, estuaries and other feeding grounds.

The size and shape of individual hunting ranges will vary within a species owing to a number of factors, such as the local status of the species, and topography and vegetation. The population density may vary and this will have an effect on the size of individual hunting ranges. Scottish Golden Eagles have hunting ranges of between 25 and 72 km², but in California the same species' home range is larger and varies between 49 and 153 km². In Michigan, where Hen Harriers are common, the average home range is 2.59 km², but the same species in Orkney has an average hunting range that is half as large again. Similar differences are found within a few hundred kilometres as well as over several thousand kilometres. The density of Peregrines within the British Isles varies between those in Wales and those on the south coast of England. In many districts there is 4.8 km between Peregrine nests with sitting pairs defending up to 1.6 km from the eyrie; on the cliffs of south-east Kent, East Sussex and Dorset, however, only about 0.5 km divides nests.

Larger birds of prey generally need larger home ranges than smaller raptors. The more open the country, the more frequent are the opportunities to see rivals, so that raptors of open country will maintain larger home ranges than those in steep and broken country or woodland. The Gyrfalcon in the tundra of the Arctic may have a hunting range as great as 500 km².

Soaring some 150 m above the ground this Gyrfalcon is hunting birds and small mammals. Its hunting range may be up to 500 km².

Where there is a big size difference between males and females, their hunting ranges may be different. Ian Newton's extensive study on Sparrowhawks, using tiny radio transmitters, showed that the birds' range depended on time of year, food supply and habitat, as well as the sex and social status of the individual. In one of the most extreme examples, in localities only 15 km apart, a well-established adult male in the weeks before egg-laying covered a range of 10 ha while a young female in winter in poor habitat covered 35 km², a

Hunting ranges of Sparrowhawks vary greatly and depend on the availability of food, the sex of the individual bird and the season.

350-fold difference. Female Sparrowhawks of established pairs tend to range much further than their mates, except during the period when they are confined to their nests.

Outside the breeding season some raptors will remain near their nests. Golden Eagles, which mate until one of the pair dies, use the same nest or alternate nests from year to year and will spend the whole year in the same vicinity. Other species, while not undertaking long migrations, will move to other areas where food may be more plentiful. These wanderers may join with other birds of prey and search for food in loose flocks. The wintering Red Kites at Tregaron in Wales are an example of this behaviour.

Migrants in their winter quarters may take up hunting territories, which they may not defend vigorously but which other raptors may avoid. These may be held for a few days until the individual moves on. Others, such as Lesser Kestrel and Red-footed Falcon spend the winter in flocks, feeding and roosting together. The Buzzards in Sweden practise an unusual form of age-related migration: the immature birds stay in the territories in which they hatched, while the adults move south to France and other parts of Europe; when the adults return, the surviving immatures move to the edges of the hunting ranges, waiting for a vacancy to occur in an established pair.

FINDING FOOD

A t the top of the food chain, raptors can choose from a vast range
of prey. Each specializes in particular types of prey and hunting
methods. Hunters of birds and flying insects often catch them in the
air, but they may also snatch them from perches or the ground.
Mammals and reptiles are hunted from perches, by hovering, by
soaring or by flying slowly above the ground. Not all raptors kill
their food: some prefer carrion, while several species will steal prey
from other predators when the opportunity occurs.

Eyesight

Of all their senses, diurnal raptors rely primarily on their keen eyesight. To hunt fast-moving prey in daylight they must be able to see
the prey and judge accurately its distance. Because the prey moves
quickly they must be capable of rapid and continuous focusing: for
example, relatively small, fast-flying insects such as dragonflies and
summer chafers are successfully hunted in flight by Hobbies.

Most birds of prey hunt initially from a stationary or almost
stationary position. Most obvious of these is a perch, but they will
also use the wind and air currents to remain stationary in the air,
hovering like the Kestrel or the Short-toed Eagle. Vultures, whose prey
does not move, soar slowly high in the sky, searching for a carcase on
the ground, the movement of another vulture towards a carcase, or
the tell-tale movement of Magpies and other corvids around carrion.

A bird that hovers is effectively stationary in the sky. A soaring
Buzzard loses some accuracy through movement, but it can still see
rabbits and mice at 100 m and more, and a Golden Eagle may hunt
hares from soaring more than 3 km up. Brown and Amadon calculated that a soaring vulture with presumed visual acuity similar to
that of a Golden Eagle would be able to see a metre-long carcase at
almost 6.5 km. Such an ability would also enable it to spot another
vulture descending to a carcase at twice that distance.

The ability of a raptor to see its prey is remarkable in comparison
with human eyesight. It may not be able to see further than we can,
or in different, improved colours, but it certainly sees detail very
much more clearly. Leslie Brown recalled seeing an Augur Buzzard,
a close African relative of the European Buzzard, swoop from a tree
100 m away to take a green grasshopper about 2.5 cm long. Brown
took a similar grasshopper and placed it on a fence post. He then
walked away and approached it slowly. He saw it in its prominent
position at between 30 and 31 m. The Augur Buzzard had seen it at
three times that distance and among vegetation, possibly partly
obscured by leaves. This suggests that the visual acuity of the Augur

Hunting birds need excellent eyesight, which may be as much as eight times better than human eyesight. This Peregrine shows how large a raptor's eyes are in comparison with the overall size of its head.

Buzzard was at least three times that of man. Other authorities have suggested that the factor of difference may be as much as eight.

Once a bird has spotted its prey, it must catch it. Like a skilled tennis player who never takes an eye off the ball, the raptor keeps its eye fixed on its prey, even though it is travelling fast. A stooping Peregrine, helped by the force of gravity, has been clocked at 402 kph (275 mph). Its intended prey would be flying at a different speed and on a different course, requiring the falcon constantly to readjust its focus. Even a Griffon Vulture, once it has seen a carcase or another vulture making for a carcase, will drop at 160 kph (100 mph). This speed is presumably necessary to ensure that the bird arrives while there is enough left to eat: there may be advantages in flocks finding food, but when they reach the kill it is every vulture for itself.

Compared with either the Peregrine or the Griffon Vulture, the Sparrowhawk has very little time in which to see its prey when it uses its technique of stealth and surprise. The alarm call of a Blackbird will scatter all the small birds in the vicinity of a hunting Sparrowhawk, so to be successful the hawk must stay hidden until the last moment. When ambushing other birds it has about three seconds in which to strike, if the prey is not to escape. During that time a combination of skills is needed: it must spot its prey, focus on it and not lose sight of it, at the same time avoiding the twigs and branches of the close country in which it operates.

In more open country, pitted against a flock of small birds, the Sparrowhawk still needs first-class eyesight. Although it may lock its eyes on a chosen individual, the hawk can be confused by the flock bunching together and zigzagging. The longer the chase continues, the greater the confusion and the smaller the chance of a kill.

Hearing

When prey cannot be seen, the predator's hearing may be important in locating it. The stealthy Sparrowhawk in closely wooded country listens for sounds that may indicate food. It can recognize distress calls, and ringers have noticed that Sparrowhawks will approach when they hear the calls of birds being extracted from mist-nets. The sounds of birds moving in the undergrowth may also attract a Sparrowhawk's attention, just as the sound of a Sparrowhawk crashing through a hedgerow will attract the attention of the birdwatcher.

In appearance, the most owl-like of the raptors are the harriers. They are the only European diurnal birds of prey to share with owls two characteristics that improve their ability to hear: large external ear openings, and a facial disc that helps to direct sound towards the ears. For nocturnal owls the need for good hearing is obvious. Harriers, too, need to hear unseen prey: to find small mammals hidden in long grass, albeit in daylight, good hearing is important.

Tawny Eagles in India and Africa learned to associate the sound of gunshot with food, according to Brown and Amadon, who presumed that the eagles were risking a close encounter with human beings bearing guns in the hope of picking up wounded or dead birds.

FLYING TECHNIQUES

Flying is a way of life for all raptors. Hunting, displaying (both to attract mates and to deter intruders) and migrating are all dependent on the birds' ability to fly. The standard flapping, direct or active flight that all birds use to get from place to place is eschewed whenever possible by raptors, which prefer to use less effort. By comparison with the frantically whirring flight of ducks, which stop flapping only when they are about to land, the progress through the air of a raptor is stately.

Wings are flapped, but sparingly. Direct flight is used when a raptor intends to reach a particular destination as quickly as possible.

The Kestrel will soar on the rising air along the slope of a motorway embankment and will glide from a perch in search of prey.

Look carefully, and the flapping raptor may well be carrying food to a plucking post. It will be moving its wings with deep powerful strokes aimed at lifting it and its cargo well clear of the ground. A Kestrel that strikes a vole on the ground will have to stop and lift off the ground. Similarly, an Osprey plunging after a fish will need maximum effort to overcome the drag of the water, especially if hampered by the added load of a squirming fish. Sometimes overeating will dictate added effort from a predator: a vulture that has gorged on a carcase may need to take a run and flap very vigorously to become airborne.

Other birds are as able to recognize the tell-tale shape of a raptor as are birdwatchers. Crows in particular seem to delight in mobbing them, possibly on the basis that attack is the best form of defence or possibly because a mobbed predator might drop its prey. Very often the raptor ignores the attentions of the attacker, almost seeming to shrug it off, but sometimes it will fly out of the way of the intruder. Occasionally it will retaliate: a Goshawk that approached too close to a White-tailed Eagle was grabbed and eaten.

Species that dive at their prey often use the momentum of the dive to continue moving forward with the prey. The Peregrine uses the momentum of its high-speed stoop to sweep upwards, carrying its prey to the perch, where it will pluck it.

Soaring

All raptors soar at times, saving energy by exploiting air currents. Soaring can be defined as gliding on rising air currents. It is an extremely effective method of energy-saving when hunting, migrating or displaying to a mate. Air rises when it meets an obstacle, if it is warmer than the surrounding air, or when wind meets an obstacle such as a cliff. When a bird glides along the windward side of the obstacle this is called slope-soaring and it is what gulls and other seabirds do along a cliff face. Kestrels have been presented with an opportunity for slope-soaring with the comparatively recent construction of embankments along motorways. Griffon Vultures in Spain have long exploited slope-soaring in the sierras, and Red Kites in mid Wales slope-soar along the edges of woods and hillsides.

On the leeward side of the slope there are waves of air rising even higher, but these are less easy to find and are exploited mainly by the real experts among the soaring birds, such as vultures. Raptors soar more frequently on thermals of warm air which rise from the ground as it heats up. Thermals occur where the ground heats more quickly than the surrounding air. The warm earth heats the air nearest to it, and the warmed air rises as a column. The cooler air that it displaces becomes a vortex around the warm air, and the bird, therefore, has to remain within the column of hot air if it, too, is to rise. When hunting, the slowly spiralling bird has an excellent all-round view. When migrating, there is a need to cover distance, so the bird leaves the thermal and glides off in the required direction, gradually losing height until it sees another bird exploiting a thermal or finds one itself. Although this is a slow method of progression, for large birds it conserves energy very well and is much more energy-efficient than flapping flight. It is possible for a vulture or large eagle to travel many kilometres, rising on one thermal, gliding to the next one and rising again, without ever flapping its wings.

Hovering

The slower a bird flies, the easier it is for it to focus on potential prey. Some raptors slow their flight to a hover, flapping their wings quickly and exploiting the wind to maintain lift. The tail is spread to act both as a brake and as a rudder, keeping the bird head-to-wind. A bird hovering and holding its head steady is effectively remaining stationary, making it easier for it to focus on any creature moving on the ground. Several species hover partially or occasionally, but the real expert is the Kestrel, which hovers in pursuit of small mammals, lizards and large insects, as does the Short-toed Eagle, which preys upon snakes and slow-worms.

Shapes in flight

The shapes of raptors in flight demonstrate their adaptations to particular ways of life. They can be divided into seven basic shapes.

Vultures Although all raptors can soar, vultures are the experts. They have a distinctive shape: long-winged with the leading and trailing edges almost parallel. The 'fingered' wingtips reduce turbulence and help balance in the air. The head is prominent and the tail short.

Head-on views of raptors show how species hold their wings at different angles when soaring. From the top: Griffon Vulture (almost flat), Golden Eagle (shallow 'V'), Hen Harrier ('V'), Goshawk (flat).

ABOVE *Griffon Vultures have 'fingered' wings which prevent their stalling at low speeds. These are the first birds to arrive at a carcase, gliding and slowing down before landing by spilling air through their wingtips.*
OPPOSITE *A soaring Peregrine holds its wings in the shallow 'V' that is typical of the larger falcons.*

Eagles Eagles are large soaring birds whose long, broad wings have 'fingertips'. The head is prominent and the tail longer than that of vultures. Eagles are long-lived, with great variations in plumage as they mature. Their wings are held flat or almost flat when soaring.

Buzzards In many ways flying buzzards are miniatures of large eagles, but their heads are smaller and the wings relatively broader with a curved trailing edge. True buzzards soar with wings raised, but Honey Buzzards soar on flat wings.

Harriers and kites Harriers are medium-sized raptors with long fingered wings and long tails. Kites are larger than harriers, approximately the size of a Buzzard, with forked tails and angular wings. Harriers soar and glide with wings held in a shallow 'V', and will also hold their wings flat when gliding. Kites soar and glide on slightly arched wings.

Hawks Short, rounded wings and long tails characterize the Sparrowhawks and Goshawks, and are adaptations that make these birds such lethal hunters in close country.

Falcons The wings of falcons are long and pointed, often held in a scythe-like shape. The tail length varies. Typically falcons hold their wings in a shallow bow when soaring and gliding.

FEEDING REQUIREMENTS

The amount of food that a bird of prey requires varies among species and between sexes. It depends on the season of the year: in warm conditions they eat less than they do in cold, when food provides the energy that keeps them warm. Larger raptors eat more than those of smaller species, but they consume a smaller proportion compared with their body weight. Thus, the daily intake varies between 6 per cent of body weight in large eagles and 25 per cent in the small raptors.

In captivity a male Sparrowhawk with a weight of about 150 g consumes 40–50 g each day, while the larger female, weighing about 270 g, takes 50–70 g. Ian Newton calculates that over the year the male would take 16.5 kg and the female 22 kg. As a breeding pair successfully rearing young, they would take 55 kg, the equivalent of 2200 House Sparrows.

A Peregrine with a body weight of 683 g requires about 53 g of food per day (8.6 per cent). The much larger Golden Eagle, with an average body weight of 4047 g, eats 251 g a day (6.25 per cent). The individual items of the Peregrine's prey are smaller and lighter than the eagle's and, therefore, a greater part of them is edible. Up to 20 per cent by weight of the eagle's prey may be inedible matter in the form of bones and fur.

Most Golden Eagles maintain hunting ranges that would provide theoretically far more food than is necessary to feed themselves and their young: in some cases this may be as much as thirty times larger than necessary, but is more usually between ten and 21 times.

Generally, predators do not have any real lasting effect on the populations of their prey, but a drop in prey populations can cause predator numbers to fall. Predation may, however, have local effects on prey. In the United States, it was found that hawks on migration did have a measurable effect on populations of their prey, but the populations recovered during the following breeding season. Lack of predators does not seem to result in any increase in numbers of their prey. As Newton has pointed out, when Sparrowhawks disappeared from large parts of England during the peak period of organochlorine pollution in the 1960s and 1970s there was no obvious increase in the populations of songbird species on which Sparrowhawks most commonly prey. One of the factors that limits the effects of raptors is that they select injured or abnormal birds as prey when they can: G. Rudebeck, writing in 1950, reckoned that a fifth of the birds selected by Sparrowhawks, Merlins and Peregrines came into this category. This prey would probably not survive to breed and, if not taken by a predator, would still be liable to premature death.

Human competitors for the prey of raptors find it difficult to accept that the effects of predators on prey are minimal. Usually, the persecution of raptors is because of their depredations, but sometimes simply because a raptor can interfere with a day's sport: although it may not take any birds, the mere presence of a Golden Eagle above a grouse moor can deter the game from taking off.

How much of a raptor's day is spent hunting depends on a number of factors. The size of prey is an obvious one. Insect-eating requires a greater number of kills than does eating larger vertebrates. Availability of food is another: if it is plentiful, hunting may not take long, and much of the day can be spent digesting food, preening and resting.

In cold weather raptors have to face an avian 'Catch-22'. More food is needed to fuel its body, but the cold weather can mean that less food is available and, even if the cold may make the prey slower and thus easier to catch, it may be thin. Wet weather can make hunting difficult, and during the breeding period this puts pressure on males bringing in food for their mates and young. In wet weather, the raptor may start to hunt later in the day than normal.

HUNTERS IN THE AIR

Many of the raptors that feed on other birds catch them in flight, but some are better adapted to taking avian prey on the ground. Some of these, though, still manage to snatch the odd bird in flight. The most skilful bird-hunters are those that outfly their victims.

The **Sparrowhawk's** diet consists almost entirely of birds, which are caught by a number of different techniques. Newton identifies six, the most common of which he calls short-stay-perch-hunting. The Sparrowhawk makes a series of short sorties, flying from perch to perch, pausing to locate potential prey and flying onwards. In open country the flights will be from tree to tree or copse to copse, in open woodland they will be shorter, perhaps 50 m, and in dense woodland these flights may be no more than a few metres. Each perch is chosen for the cover it affords. The flight between each one is a model of energy-conservation and concealment: the bird drops from its perch, using the momentum to glide low over the ground, and then it loses speed by sweeping upwards to its next perch.

Perched motionless in cover, a female Sparrowhawk waits in ambush
for a small bird to come within striking distance. From the cover
of the contours of a hedgerow, a male Sparrowhawk flies fast
in pursuit of a small bird.

When it spots suitable prey the hawk will, if it is close, drop all attempts at stealth and fly at full speed, 50 kph, relying on being faster over a short distance than its prey. If the prey is too far away for a high-speed dash, the hawk has to approach stealthily, leaving its perch, building up speed with a few vigorous flaps and then gliding on still, slightly curved wings, using cover where possible. The prey may be taken from the perch and, if it is aware of the hawk and flies, it may be snatched in mid-air.

Some Sparrowhawks employ high soaring and stooping, circling very high, 100 m or more, and dropping a very fast glide. This is so acutely angled that its is almost vertical in pursuit of flying birds, but if the prey is perched the dive will be shallower. Surprise and speed are the elements of this technique, which is also used to hunt finches and Starlings in flocks. This stoop is reminiscent of the Peregrine's.

Concealment is the key to contour-hugging flight. The Sparrowhawk flies fast along the edge of cover, which may be a woodland edge, stream, green lane or hedgerow, to snatch small birds.

Waiting for the prey to come to the predator, still-hunting, is the fourth technique. The hawk sits hidden near a pool or a place to which small birds are attracted. Sometimes the hawk may be resting, and taking a small bird in this way may be no more than opportunism, but Sparrowhawks have been seen to still-hunt in open areas where they would be unlikely to rest.

When a hawk knows that there is prey in an area, it will hunt by low quartering, flying very slowly a few metres above the ground and looking downwards. When it spots prey it drops with legs outstretched. With its relatively short wings the Sparrowhawk's wing-loading is high and it is unable, therefore, to fly as slowly as harriers, which use similar tactics.

The final two categories of hunting are by sound and on foot. The calls of small birds have been seen to attract Sparrowhawks, which have also been seen to enter cover in response to rustling. In thick woodland Sparrowhawks will hop from branch to branch in search of nestlings, and they have been seen to run along the ground behind cover to approach finch flocks.

Goshawks can take larger prey than can Sparrowhawks and will take mammals as well as birds. They hunt in fast, short bursts relying on speed to outfly the victim. This female is chasing a Wood Pigeon.

Falconers using trained birds have noted that trained Sparrowhawks chasing birds in the open will fly like Battle of Britain pilots in the blind spot below and behind the victim. As it closes on its prey the hawk will swing upwards and grasp it. The Sparrowhawk's agility enables it, if it is within reach, to grasp its victim even if the latter suddenly changes direction.

Having caught its prey, the Sparrowhawk carries it in its talons to a plucking post, usually in cover. Here it eviscerates the bird and, in the case of larger ones, discards feet, bill, shoulder girdle and breastbone.

In several ways the **Goshawk** is a larger version of the Sparrowhawk. However, male Goshawks and female Sparrowhawks may overlap in size. The size and species of their prey may also overlap, but the Goshawk also takes large birds, such as Pheasants and Hazel Grouse, and mammals such as Red Squirrel. Despite the similarities in behaviour and prey, there are differences in the shapes of the two species. The Goshawk has a distinctly 'S'-shaped trailing edge to

Surprise is the key to the Bonelli's Eagle's hunting technique. It flies from the cover of a tree, catching its prey on the ground or, as is the case with this Red-legged Partridge, as it takes off.

each wing and the wingtips appear to be relatively narrower than the Sparrowhawk's. Its flight is powerful, with slower wingbeats than those of the Sparrowhawk and a tendency to intersperse flaps with glides on flat or slightly bowed wings.

When hunting, the Goshawk will fly fast in pursuit of its prey, but rarely for more than 500 m. It also uses cover either to approach prey or to wait for the prey to come within stooping distance. When hunting Feral Pigeons, it uses a Peregrine-like stoop from a great height.

Once it has caught and killed its prey the Goshawk carries it to cover where it is plucked and eaten on the ground or a convenient hummock. In the nesting season, the food may be taken to a branch near the nest or a nearby disused nest.

Hobbies are specialists in hunting birds, large insects and bats in flight. This Hobby, having chosen a House Martin as a victim, flies behind it in the martin's blind spot.

Bonelli's Eagle is a large opportunist predator that takes mammals, birds and occasionally reptiles. Most of its prey is caught on the ground, but some birds are killed as they are flushed. Bonelli's Eagle hunts from the cover of trees and will quarter ground in search of prey. It will also stoop from soaring, but it does this less than do other large predators. This eagle follows habitual hunting routes, returning to the same place each day.

Although the **Montagu's Harrier** will usually take prey from the ground, it is more likely to take flying birds than either the Hen or the Marsh Harrier. It flies low along the edge of vegetation and may fly up and down transects across large open areas. Sometimes it will pursue flying birds and overhaul them.

Several falcons specialize in hunting other birds. In the Western Palearctic the smallest falcon is the **Merlin**, which in the breeding season feeds on moorland songbirds such as Meadow Pipits, Wheatears and Skylarks. It hunts these by flying low from a perch in level flight, gliding in for the kill at a height of about 1 m, striking prey on or near the ground. The prey is taken to a plucking post with a good all-round view, decapitated and partially skinned, and eaten. During the breeding season, the food may be concealed in the vicinity of the nest for future use.

Almost all of the food of the **Hobby** is caught on the wing. This is one of the more crepuscular of the region's raptors, being particularly active in the evening when large insects and bats emerge and small birds go to roost. It will wait to stoop from a great height, or it may drop below the prey and take it on an upward swoop, which has the twin advantages of unsighting the victim and silhouetting it against the sky. The prey is grabbed with the feet and may be eaten in flight, but will more probably be taken to a perch to be plucked and eaten.

Well-fed migrant songbirds, such as this Yellow Wagtail, crossing the Mediterranean in late summer and autumn, are an important source of food for Eleonora's Falcons.

At least seventy species of birds have been recorded in the diet of European Hobbies, and they may account for many of the escaped Budgerigars in southern England and parts of Germany. Hirundines are an important part of the summer diet of the Hobby, and there is a superficial similarity in shape between it and its prey.

By delaying its breeding season and switching from insects to birds, **Eleonora's Falcon** takes advantage of the small migrants that cross the Mediterranean in late summer and autumn. To stoke up for their flight southwards across the Mediterranean and then the Sahara Desert, migrating warblers almost double their weight, a fact which is welcomed by both the southern European hunters and Eleonora's Falcons that breed on the islands of the Mediterranean and Aegean. The falcon lays its eggs later than most raptors in order that the hatching of the young coincides with the passage of the migrants.

Eleonora's Falcons breed in loose colonies on the cliffs and hunt communally. They face into the wind and soar above the top of the cliffs to a height of about 1000 m. As the migrants make for land, the falcons stoop. If they miss, they will make another attempt or fly in pursuit. Nevertheless the odds are in favour of the migrants: the success rate of the falcons' stooping has been put at less than 50 per cent by Hartmut Walter.

Hunting Eleonora's Falcons fly with fast, regular wingbeats, but their wing action is slower than that of the Hobby. Their wings are also longer and appear narrower than those of the smaller Hobby. They are more slender than the larger Peregrine, whose chunkiness is very apparent if you see the two species in the air together.

The largest European falcon is the **Gyrfalcon**, which feeds mainly on medium-sized birds, most of which are probably taken on the ground. It flies fast and direct at between 6 and 20 m, gaining height for the final stoop, which may be very fast. It will also stoop from up to 300 m. Prey is plucked on the spot, or carried a short distance. If it is taken to the nest it is usually decapitated, but the falcon only does this in the breeding season. It seems to need up to 300 g a day and may not kill daily, feeding for up to a week on previous kills.

The Gyrfalcon, feeds on birds which it hunts by flying at between 6 and 20 m above the ground, rising fast to a height of 300 m for the stoop.

Almost all the prey taken by **Peregrines** is birds, most of which are taken on the wing. Potential prey is spotted from a high circling flight or from a high vantage point such as a cliff, tree or hill. The Peregrines that live on western coasts are able to use the updraughts above cliff faces to 'wait on'. The Peregrine flies in pursuit of the prey and then climbs above to stoop with wings folded and held back from the body. The speed of the stoop has been estimated as 402 kph, its velocity often making it lethal. The prey is struck with the hind claw just behind the head. If this fails to kill the prey the bill is used to bite through the base of the neck. A Peregrine's stoop and kill all happen so quickly that it is very easy for the observer to miss parts of the action. The problem is whether to watch the Peregrine or the prey. If you choose the latter, you have to be sure that the bird you are watching is the selected victim. Peregrines seem to single out individual birds and experienced Peregrine-watchers like Cornishman Dick Treleaven can identify which is most likely to be picked out. If you choose to watch the Peregrine, you have to take into account that it might be hunting in co-operation with its mate.

Sometimes, when the Peregrine has missed on its first stoop, it turns and chases the prey, which often flies low and jinks. Often this is a contest of speed and the prey may outfly the predator, but if two Peregrines are working as a team the second one may approach from an oblique angle and take the prey by surprise.

The proportion of unsuccessful stoops is high, perhaps 80 per cent, although some may be playful rather than serious. As Bruce Pearson and Robert Burton have pointed out, if the Peregrine was always successful, falconry would soon have lost its appeal.

The Peregrine has preferred plucking posts to which it takes its prey. Here the brains and breast are eaten first. It may take up to an hour for the Peregrine to consume its prey, but usually it has disposed of it in between ten and thirty minutes.

Only the very largest of birds escape the attentions of Peregrines. The range of species recorded as prey is remarkable: the smallest is the Goldcrest and the largest the Grey Heron. This variety results from the differences in availability of food, from place to place and from season to season. Two of the most frequently recorded species are Feral Pigeons and Starlings, which are often taken in winter by Peregrines that breed in towns.

The Peregrine's penchant for pigeons earned it persecution in the name of the war effort in the early 1940s. Homing pigeons were carried by RAF planes operating over the Western Approaches and

Almost all the Peregrine's prey consists of birds which are taken in flight. The hunting falcon hangs on the wind, high above its prey, waiting with wings held back to stoop at great speed.

ABOVE *Lanners take a wide range of birds, both in the air and on the ground. Here one stoops on a Cream-coloured Courser.* BELOW *Sakers take small mammals and birds. This Saker is stooping on a Wheatear.*

were released in the event of the aircraft ditching in the sea. Anxious that the pigeons should not fall victim to Peregrines as they reached the British coastline, the Air Ministry ordered the destruction of Peregrines. This campaign was not so devastating to the Peregrine populations as the use of DDT and other organochlorine chemicals in the 1950s and 1960s, when numbers plummeted. Today, some pigeon-fanciers again want steps taken against Peregrines, which they see as a major cause of losses of racing pigeons. Weather and disorientation, however, probably cause far greater losses than do Peregrines.

The re-establishment of the Peregrine has also caused conservationists some philosophical problems. Peregrines feed close to their breeding eyries, and, if these happen to be near colonies of birds that are easy prey, the raptors will have no hesitation in taking them. Thus, in Wales, conservationists have to grit their teeth and watch Peregrines which breed near a seabird colony taking Roseate and Arctic Terns, both species that are diminishing in numbers.

Slightly smaller and less thickset than the Peregrine, the **Barbary Falcon** is another bird-hunter. It is faster even than the Peregrine, whose hunting techniques are similar, but it does not take so wide a range of species, appearing to concentrate on doves, partridges and songbirds in its North African and Middle Eastern desert habitat.

The **Lanner** is larger than the Peregrine, except the race found in north-west Africa. Its wings seem longer and narrower but with more rounded tips, and its tail is proportionally longer. When waiting on, it soars high on flat or slightly lowered wings, but it stoops with enormous speed on prey below it. Another technique is to chase its prey in low direct flight with determined wingbeats, more rapid and deeper than when it is merely travelling from one point to another. Its hunting success in rocky terrain is said by Mebs to be 13 per cent.

One of the largest falcons of the region is the **Saker**. Its wingspan is not far short of a Buzzard's. Its wings are broad, but longer than a Peregrine's, and its tail is longer. Most prey is taken on the ground, but it will stoop, often not from a great height, on flying birds.

PREY ON THE GROUND

Catching prey on the ground is not so dramatic as snatching a flying bird in mid-flight, and for the birdwatcher the outcome is often less easy to determine, because in many cases the human observer does not have an uninterrupted view of the ground and the kill is obscured from view by cover.

Kites, among the most catholic of raptors in their diet, usually catch and kill their prey on the ground. The smallest of the three breeding species in the Western Palearctic is the **Black-winged Kite**.

Because it hovers in search of small mammals, birds, reptiles and insects it is reminiscent of a large, pale Kestrel, but it is much more graceful. It also quarters the ground, flying with a series of flaps and long glides. As it drops, its wings are held high above its back, their angle varied to control the descent; about a metre above the ground the wings are raised and the kite drops on its prey. It may also hunt prey from a perch.

The **Black Kite** eats whatever animal material it can find – dead or alive, furred, feathered or scaled, vertebrate or invertebrate. It is bold, wary and has learned to exploit the sources of food available to it. To find food it flies slowly and relatively low, 6–10 m from the ground. When it spots food, it will swoop very swiftly to grab it in its claws. Small items are consumed in flight, but larger morsels will be taken to a habitually used feeding place. In the Middle East and India, particularly, it shows little fear of people, snatching food from market stalls and unattended tables.

The slightly larger **Red Kite** also takes a wide variety of food, but is not so widespread as the Black Kite. It soars in circles over open ground, sometimes at several hundred metres, diving steeply when prey is located and grasping it in its talons. It is not always successful and may pursue its prey on foot, but the chases do not last long. Rodents, other small mammals and young birds, especially of species that breed on the ground or in the open, are the kite's main food.

Four species of harrier are found in the region. All share a similar basic shape, but their ways of life are sufficiently different for them not to compete. These differences in behaviour are reflected in the differences in shape.

The largest and most stocky is the **Marsh Harrier**, which also has longer and broader wings than the other harriers. It is found in wetlands with large reedbeds and marshes, and its food is mainly small mammals and birds taken in the reeds. Its hunting flight is not swift, about 30 kph, and the wingbeats are rather heavy, usually between five and ten followed by a glide. The wings are held in a very shallow 'V' for the glide. When the harrier spots a small mammal or bird, it drops, claws spread to grab it. Sometimes hunting flight is interrupted by hovering, particularly when high winds provide additional lift.

Marsh Harriers are summer migrants to Britain, and in parts of the country where they are increasing in numbers, such as eastern Suffolk, they may be seen flying over other habitats. However, it is in continental Europe that they present identification difficulties because they are often seen there in the same habitats as Black Kites. Confusions may also occur between female and immature Marsh Harriers and dark-phase Booted Eagles, dark Buzzards and dark Honey Buzzards when soaring and on migration, but their hunting techniques are very different. When soaring, the Marsh Harrier will hold its wings in a shallow 'V', while all of the others except the Buzzard soar on flat wings, and the Buzzard glides on flat wings. In silhouette, the Marsh Harrier has a longer tail and wings that are longer and appear narrower than those of the Buzzard.

In the Western Palearctic, **Hen Harriers** are found breeding on moorland and wintering in open country, such as farmland and coastal sand-dunes. (In the New World, this species is known as the Marsh Hawk and favours, as its name suggests, a wetter habitat.)

In silhouette, the Hen Harrier is slimmer than the Marsh Harrier. It is also more agile, which enables it to take more manoeuvrable prey such as songbirds. The main food is small mammals, particularly voles. The grey male is smaller than the female and takes smaller birds. It has been suggested that the grey plumage camouflages the bird against the sky, a hunting advantage needed by the male as the main provider of food when the young are in the nest.

If you see a Hen Harrier flying high, it is not hunting. When seeking prey, the harrier flies 3–9 m above the ground at 20–30 kph. Its method is a painstaking quartering of the ground. If there is a head wind the speed of the flight may be slower, and the bird can glide or flap-and-glide instead of steady flapping flight. When it spots a small mammal, the hunting bird turns, fans its tail, stalls and drops; it will rise with the prey within a few minutes if successful. In winter, a female Hen Harrier needs four Meadow Pipits or two Orkney Voles each day to survive. A Red Grouse, which will probably be taken only if injured or sick, will feed it for two or three days.

When the Hen Harrier is hunting mammals, it ignores birds. When in search of birds it flies faster, at over 40 kph. Some birds may be taken in flight, but usually they are taken on the ground. Donald Watson watched a male hunt over a five-year-old forestry plantation for two hours without making a successful kill, but he saw another catch three voles on moorland in the space of twenty minutes.

While Marsh Harriers are found at reedbeds in flat country and Hen Harriers prefer moorland and open farmland, the **Montagu's Harrier** chooses an intermediate habitat of cereal fields, grassland and the edges of wetland. There are parts of the Dutch polders and eastern France where there is a good chance of seeing all three species during the breeding season (*see* pages 132 and 134).

Montagu's Harriers are noticeably slimmer than either of the previously described species. Their long narrow wings give them an appearance not dissimilar at a distance to that of a Kestrel. Active flight is buoyant and consists of five or so wing-beats followed by a somewhat uncertain, butterfly-like glide. When hunting, this harrier flies a few metres from the ground along fixed routes at about 30 kph. On sighting prey, it checks and drops to the ground. It will hover to spot prey and sometimes watches from a fixed perch.

Its food is mainly rodents and birds, particularly in the breeding season, but there are geographical differences: in the Vendée, the south of France and central Spain large insects are an important part of the diet, but in western Spain, Hungary and Kazakhstan lizards may account for almost half the food brought to the nest.

A fourth harrier is also to be found in the region. In late summer, **Pallid Harriers** move from their breeding grounds on the steppes of the Ukraine, Russia and Kazakhstan to India and Africa. Most winter in India, but there are passages through the eastern part of the Western Palearctic in March and April and in September and October. A few individuals overwinter in Greece, Israel and Egypt. Their habitat is open and they hunt at a height of 1–9 m. Small mammals and birds are taken on the ground in a quick pounce.

Male Pallid Harriers are smaller and lighter than females, their flight even more buoyant than Montagu's, and their pale grey plumage giving them an almost tern-like appearance. The species' food is predominantly mammalian, but some birds are eaten when rodents are in short supply. The species taken tend to be those that live on the ground, such as larks, pipits and quails.

Buzzards hunt in several ways. Here one drops from a perch to take prey on the ground. The other flies along a field edge in search of prey.

Long-legged Buzzards hunt mainly small mammals, reptiles and large insects for which it searches in circling flight up to 30 m from the ground. It holds its wings in a 'V'.

Sparrowhawks are principally hunters in close cover, but they will prey on bird flocks in open fields. I have watched a female in winter drop steeply from her perch in a large ash and fly fast and low, perhaps no more than 1 m above the ground, some 30 m across pasture in which a mixed flock of Fieldfares and Redwings was feeding. It seemed as though she had already selected an individual Fieldfare, because she flew over several birds, ignoring them as they took to the air, and took her victim on the ground.

Its adaptability in diet has made the **Buzzard** one of the most common raptors in Europe, widespread through all suitable habitat except in the UK where the efforts of gamekeepers seem to have confined it to the south-west and the Welsh Marches. The wooded landscape interspersed with the farmland of temperate Europe is an ideal habitat for the Buzzard, whose food includes small mammals, birds, reptiles, frogs, and insects and other invertebrates, which are usually taken alive but may on occasions be taken as carrion.

The Buzzard sights its food in three principal ways, apparently dictated to some extent by the restrictions of particular habitats.

Voles and lemmings are the principal prey in Scandinavia of the Rough-legged Buzzard which hunts them by hovering, quartering the ground, or, as is shown here, from a low perch.

It uses high perches such as trees, telegraph poles or high rocks as vantage points, and may wait on such a perch for several hours, scanning the terrain. Once prey is located the Buzzard glides down on to it very quickly, sometimes using cover to approach. Buzzards will also search for prey in flight, soaring, hanging on a head wind or hovering at a height of up to 100 m and swooping down on the victim. Insects, other invertebrates and even small mammals may be hunted on foot, the Buzzard stalking through the grass like a huge Song Thrush.

The French name for the Buzzard is *Buse Variable* and, particularly in continental Europe, the species' plumage is very variable, ranging from a pale cream as to seem white in the distance to a Van Dyck brown so dark that it looks almost black. Their medium size and their not very distinctive shape do not make it easy to separate buzzards from other medium-sized raptors. They hold their wings up in a 'V' when soaring, and the wingtips curve upwards. Confusion can arise with the Honey Buzzard, but the latter has a longer, more pigeon-like head and a longer tail.

In the east of the region and in North Africa is another buzzard, slightly larger than the Common Buzzard. This is the **Long-legged Buzzard**, which because of its size appears more eagle-like. It soars on wings held in a deeper 'V' than the Buzzard's. When hunting, it circles at about 30 m, gliding and soaring, dropping to the ground when it sights prey; its hunting flight is sometimes interrupted by the bird hovering. Like the Common Buzzard, the Long-legged perches on telegraph poles and crags to spot prey. At times it will also hunt on the ground, stalking large insects and waiting outside the burrows of rodents. The food includes small mammals up to the size of hares, but usually smaller, and lizards, frogs and toads.

The **Rough-legged Buzzard** is of a similar size to the Long-legged Buzzard, but it breeds in the tundra around the Arctic and winters across central Europe. Although it takes some birds, its main food is small mammals, particularly voles and lemmings. The populations of small rodents fluctuate from year to year, with dramatic results on the population of the Rough-legged Buzzards (*see* pages 112–13). It has been estimated that its daily food requirement is 10 per cent of its body weight, approximately 80–120 g or four to six small mammals. Hunting, Rough-legged Buzzards quarter open ground, hover and pounce, or hunt from a perch, stooping in a short dive to the ground.

Most birdwatchers who have seen the **Lesser Spotted Eagle** have done so when it is migrating. It breeds in remote woodland in eastern Europe and the Balkans and winters in East Africa. Most of its prey is small mammals taken on the ground. The eagle hunts in slow gliding flight, quartering the ground, pausing almost motionless to take prey by pouncing. Sometimes it will hunt prey from a perch and may stalk prey on foot. Dr Meyburg, Germany's leading raptor specialist, found that they hunt for three hours or so from 7 a.m., again from noon for two hours and again at 7 p.m.

In the west of its Eurasian range the **Spotted Eagle** overlaps with the Lesser Spotted Eagle, but their choices of habitat and of food differ. The Spotted Eagle prefers lowland forest near water, and it prefers bodies of water at all times of year.

The Spotted Eagle is not a dramatic hunter. Much bulkier than the Lesser Spotted Eagle, it is described by Porter *et al.*, in the indispensable *Flight Identification of European Raptors* as 'not unlike a miniature White-tailed [Eagle]'. It hunts on the wing with a slow gliding flight, quartering the ground and stopping when it sights prey. It drops on slow-moving prey, or carrion. When hunting Coots on water it will fly low over the surface, separating and snatching one individual from the flock. It will also stalk insects, amphibians and wounded animals on the ground. It can move quickly on the ground, and in the early part of the century Colonel Meinertzhagen recorded seeing one running 50 m in pursuit of a wounded duck.

White-tailed Eagles will pursue divers and sea-ducks, such as these Eiders. The ducks are snatched from the surface, but they may survive by diving beneath it. The eagle may persist until the duck becomes exhausted. One Eider was seen to dive 65 times before being caught.

There are discrete populations of the **Tawny Eagle** resident in north-west Africa, but most live in sub-Saharan Africa. The **Steppe Eagle** is sometimes considered as a race of the same species; it breeds in the Russian steppes and winters in Iran, Iraq and Saudi Arabia and down the eastern side of Africa, occasionally wintering in Greece, Turkey and Israel.

Despite these two eagles' very close relationship, their hunting techniques differ. The Steppe Eagle, which hunts between 7 and 10 a.m. and 7 and 10 p.m., does so principally by soaring at a height of some 150–200 m and dropping on its prey or, on the steppes, waiting in ambush outside the burrows of Susliks. The Tawny Eagle in Africa prefers to stoop from short flights or from a perch. It may also skim low over the ground and pounce on prey. A variety of food is taken by Tawny and Steppe Eagles. In the breeding season the latter concentrates on Susliks and hares.

While the Golden Eagle is found in more mountainous areas, the **Imperial Eagle** prefers the lowlands where woods merge with open country. This large raptor is not agile and consequently takes its prey mainly on the ground. The range of prey taken is large, from Striped Field Mice to Great Bustards, with mammals predominating over birds. Imperial Eagles spend many hours soaring high or perched high in trees searching for prey.

A huge folklore has built up around the **Golden Eagle** and its food. The romantically inclined Victorians enjoyed the idea of its attacking and killing adult Red Deer: the King of the Birds takes on the Monarch of the Glen. But, although remains of adult deer have been found at eagles' eyries, the only records of the Golden Eagle taking live Red Deer relate to calves. As with other species of raptor that take carrion as well as live prey, it is easy to draw the wrong conclusion from the remains at an eyrie.

Although it soars in search of food, the Golden Eagle rarely stoops from a great height, preferring to fly low, flushing the prey from cover and striking it on the ground. Brown Hares form an important part of its diet, and the eagle sometimes brushes the tops of the heather with its talons and wingtips as it takes them. When grouse are flushed, the eagle may fly in pursuit and take the prey near the ground in flight.

Another large eagle that relies on surprise and takes prey from the ground is the **White-tailed Eagle**. Prey, which may be as large as Whooper Swans, is spotted while the eagle is motionless on a perch, while soaring to a height of 300 m or from a low direct flight over water. The eagle sometimes hovers before gliding in for the kill with talons outstretched. At other times it may dive steeply from soaring flight. When the prey is on the surface of water the attack may be prolonged, especially if the victim dives to escape the eagle. Bruno Liljefors' famous oil painting shows the dramatic struggle between a Black-throated Diver and a White-tailed Eagle against a swelling sea and wind. One eagle watched by John Love on Rhum glided low with the sun behind it when hunting gulls on the shore.

White-tailed Eagles are able to catch birds in flight on occasions. Meinertzhagen, for instance, saw one grab a mobbing gull in flight. The Norwegian eagle expert Dr Johans Willgohs recorded a Raven mobbing a White-tailed Eagle near its nest. It was followed by a Goshawk, which attacked from below and approached close enough to be grabbed and killed.

Eiders will be attacked continuously until they become exhausted by successive dives. One eagle forced an Eider to dive some 65 times before catching it. Sometimes exhaustion beats the eagle, and Love records one immature bird apparently tiring after 28 attempts at a Little Grebe. Eiders are heavy items of prey, and White-tailed Eagles have been seen to get airborne with a dead Eider but carrying the duck so that it drags across the surface of the sea.

Any birds at a disadvantage are likely prey for White-tailed Eagles. Moulting geese are particularly vulnerable when flightless, and the list of potential prey includes ducks wounded by gunshot and swans frozen into the ice. The disadvantage may, however, be only apparent, and the White-tailed Eagle is not always the victor. When an attempt was first made to reintroduce White-tailed Eagles to Fair Isle in the 1970s, the young, inexperienced birds soared on the updraughts along the cliff faces in search of prey. Young Fulmars in their nests on the cliffs were potential victims, but when one eagle approached, the Fulmars spat an oily substance at it and the predator was actually discovered grounded, after being drenched with Fulmar oil.

Much of the **Booted Eagle's** day is spent on the wing, soaring 30–150 m above its woodland habitat or open country. It dives fast when it spots prey, and kills birds, lizards and small mammals on the ground. It also dives into foliage and pursues its prey along the branches of trees. When flying directly, it has deeper wing-beats than the Buzzard and intersperses glides with four or five loose flaps.

Bonelli's Eagles follow regular hunting routes, often appearing daily in the same place. Most prey is taken on or near the ground, but they can catch birds on the wing. When hunting from soaring flight, the eagle folds back its wings and plummets at great speed in an angled stoop.

Bonelli's Eagles take mainly medium-sized birds and mammals, with some reptiles. Bird species, such as francolins, which spend much of their time on the ground are often grabbed as they take off. Prey is often spotted from a tree or from soaring flight. The eagle will also quarter ground in a low flight to surprise its prey. When hunting by soaring, it holds its wings flat and at right angles to the body, until prey is spotted, when the the wings are folded back and the bird stoops at great speed. In active flight its wing-beats are shallow and powerful, interspersed with glides

One of the most typical feeders on the ground is the **Kestrel**. To catch its main prey, small mammals, it has adapted to hovering flight. Usually flying at about 15–20 m or soaring, and often using the effects of slopes such as motorway embankments, it turns head-to-wind and hovers. When it spots prey, the Kestrel drops, pausing to hover again, dropping again, and finally pouncing on its victim.

Large insects, worms and other invertebrates may be hunted on foot. Kestrels hunt throughout the day, but in places where diurnal mammals are scarce they will hunt at dawn and dusk in order to take nocturnal species such as Wood Mice. During the incubation period, females tend to hunt for a brief period in late afternoon; the males may be seen hunting throughout the day.

Hunting in open steppe grasslands, the **Saker**, one of the largest falcons, feeds mainly on small mammals, for which it searches by flying low to pounce before the prey reaches cover. Susliks are the principal prey. Sometimes the falcon will sit on a prominent perch and wait for its prey to come within pouncing range.

A Saker flies low over steppe grassland hunting Susliks (Ground Squirrels), which it attempts to take unawares before they can find the safety of their burrows.

REPTILE-HUNTERS

The only true snake eagle in the Western Palearctic is the **Short-toed Eagle**. Its daily intake is one or two medium-sized snakes, which it catches in its talons. Prey is located from flight or from a perch. Haystacks, trees, telegraph-poles and ruins are all used as look-out posts, and prey appears to be particularly vulnerable when crossing roads. The Short-toed Eagle, usually flying at between 15 and 30 m, quarters open ground, pauses on the wind or hovers with wings fanning less frenetically than the Kestrel's. It will also soar on flat wings, which are raised slightly when heading into a strong wind. When it moves into a glide, the wings are held slightly upwards and arcing down to slightly drooping tips. It may swoop from greater heights. Once prey is located, the eagle plummets, pausing with legs outstretched just before striking its prey.

Small snakes and lizards are lifted immediately into the air, where the head is crushed or torn off and the body eaten in a series of gulps. The smallest are eaten head-first, the eagle feeding the snake into its bill with its feet. Larger snakes are killed on the ground and eaten there or taken back to the nest or a perch, where they are torn up and consumed.

There are obvious dangers in feeding on snakes, some of which may be venomous, and although not immune to venom, the Short-toed Eagle does have scaly legs and thick down that will give some protection against snake bites, which can be damaging whether the snake is venomous or not. It appears to be good at snake identification, and even in places where viperine species of snake are common it will avoid them, presumably because it recognizes their thick bodies and well-defined heads. Short-toed Eagles have been seen to carry vipers, but these may often be picked up when they are dead.

Totroises do not appear in the diet of many birds, but some Golden Eagles have learned to drop them to the ground to smash their shells.

Other eagles are capable of dealing with snakes. The **Spotted Eagle** hunts amphibians and reptiles on the ground and will eat grass snakes up to 60 cm long. A study in north-eastern Tatar showed 17.5 per cent of its diet was snakes, which were very common in the area.

In Spain especially, the **Booted Eagle** takes lizards, particularly ocellated lizards, which are among the larger Iberian species. These may be taken by stooping from soaring flight or from a perch.

A small accipiter that is found in the eastern Mediterranean and around the Black Sea is the **Levant Sparrowhawk**. The females are about the same size as female Sparrowhawks and the males are smaller, but the size difference between the sexes is not so great as among common Sparrowhawks. Although superficially quite similar to the latter in several ways, in flight Levant Sparrowhawks have narrower, more pointed, wings. Their main prey is lizards and large insects which are hunted by flying as slowly as possible at a height of 6–10 m and dropping on them. The Levant Sparrowhawk's legs and toes are shorter than the Sparrowhawk's and this together with the tough scales on the legs is an adaptation for catching reptiles.

Tortoises do not figure in the lists of food of many birds, but some **Golden Eagles** have learned how to break into their apparently impregnable carapaces. Records of eagles eating tortoises come from France, Bulgaria and Israel. A pair of eagles nesting near Jerusalem ate a large number of tortoises. They caught these on the ground and flew up to about 30 m before dropping them to shatter the shells. If the carapace did not shatter at the first drop, the eagle would fly up with it and drop it again. It would sometimes take several drops to crack the shell sufficiently, and on at least one occasion eight drops of the same tortoise were recorded.

Bearded Vultures, also known as Lammergeiers, habitually smash large mammal bones by dropping them from heights of 50–80 m on to rocks below. They will also take tortoises and treat them in the same fashion, carrying them up clasped in their feet: flying with the wind, the vulture the drops the tortoise, immediately turning into the wind to descend after it. In South Africa they have been seen to deal in the same way with a mammal, the rock hyrax. Black Vultures were recorded in the last century taking tortoises in Greece.

In southern Europe, where lizards are common, they may be the principal constituent of the diet of **Kestrels**. These are caught in the same way as rodents and insects on the ground: the Kestrel hovers, dropping on to its prey the moment it spots it. Given the lizards' superb camouflage against vegetation and rock surfaces, the Kestrel's visual acuity must be of a very high order. Bruce Pearson saw one Kestrel in the sub-Sahel region of Africa fly towards a nearby tree and snatch a lizard that Bruce had not seen from the trunk.

Although mainly a hunter of birds, the **Lanner** will take lizards in the desert. The larger **Saker** will also take lizards and frogs.

The omnivorous **Black Kite** will eat amphibians and reptiles if the opportunity occurs, but these comprise a much smaller proportion of its diet than do mammals, birds and fish. The **Red Kite** will also feed on reptiles and amphibians, particularly in Spain in spring and summer. **Buzzards** likewise will eat snakes, including vipers, which it presumably grasps and kills very swiftly.

FISH-EATERS

Only one raptor which breeds in Europe feeds almost exclusively on fish, and that is the Osprey. Two others which often catch fish are the White-tailed Eagle, which also scavenges for dead fish and other carcases along the shoreline, and the Black Kite, which takes fish, both dead and alive. Other raptors eat fish when scavenging.

The fishing techniques of Osprey, White-tailed Eagle and Black Kite are all different. The most dramatic is the Osprey's. Its actual catching technique is probably better known than that of any other raptor, because every detail can be seen, thanks to its choice of open water for hunting. Here there are no grasses or bushes to obscure the view of the moment of capture. Add to this the fact that its plunge is dramatic and makes good television, so that it has also been filmed frequently. The viewer, however, may be confused about the speed at which Ospreys hunt, because of the indiscriminate use of slow motion and film editors who edit together slow motion and normal speed film without telling their viewers which is which. Consequently, the fishing of the Osprey sometimes appears on television to be a much more stately affair than it is in reality.

The **Osprey** may hunt from a perch or from soaring flight 5–70 m above the water. Usually, it flies slowly above the water at a height of between 15 and 30 m. In pursuit of faster fish, such as Herring, it flies closer to the water and dives at a low angle without a hover. When it spots a fish, it slows to a hover, long enough to size up and focus on its prey. When it identifies suitable prey, the Osprey begins its dive, sometimes pausing and even pulling out of it. The wings are half-folded during much of the dive; as the bird nears the water they are spread and the feet thrust forward. The head is aligned with the spread claws, allowing the bird to keep an accurate sighting of the fish. The wings are held back as the bird enters the water, and brought forward to give it lift once the fish has been caught.

The angle of the dive is acute, between 45° and the perpendicular. The depth of the plunge depends on the depth of the fish, but is never more than a metre, unless the bird has miscalculated the size of the fish and cannot disentangle itself, in which case it may drown.

The fish is grasped in both feet, with one behind the other. The Osprey may alter the direction in which the fish faces so that it is carried head-first, which must be aerodynamically better than sideways or even tail-first. The prey is taken to a bare branch or mud-flat to be eaten. Fish as heavy as 1.2 kg have been recorded, but the more usual weights are 150–300 g. When carrying the fish and also

The Osprey is a specialist fish-hunter, hovering to spot prey and plunging towards the water with feet thrown forward at the last moment.

when eating it, a matter of perhaps thirty minutes for a hungry bird with a 300-g fish, the Osprey is vulnerable to piracy from Carrion Crows, Grey Herons, and other raptors; of these the White-tailed Eagle is the most likely to be successful. How many fish an Osprey catches in a day depends on the size of the fish and the needs of the bird. One to four fish are caught daily and individual consumption may be 200–400 g. The nest at Loch Garten in Scotland, under the protection of the RSPB for over forty years, has been intensively studied and the comings and goings at the nest recorded. The male brings an average of 2.2 fish to the nest during incubation and 4.6 during the nestling period. The most brought in one day was eleven.

A White-tailed Eagle flies low over the water. When it spots a fish, the eagle grabs it from beneath the surface with its talons.

The hunting success of an Osprey is between 15 and 30 per cent. Dr Jon Swenson discovered that the success rate was higher with slow-moving fish in shallow water than with fast-moving predatory fish. He recorded a 68 per cent success in 48 dives after flatfish. Experience seems to count, and young birds up to six months old are only half as successful as adults.

Fish make up a third of the White-tailed Eagle's food. Most are taken by plunging into the water, but the eagle will wade in shallow water after flatfish and large stranded fish.

The huge **White-tailed Eagle** is an omnivore, but its preference for a coastal habitat often means a fishy diet. It also shares the Osprey's adaptation of tiny spikes on the soles of its enormous feet. Such a large bird is not very agile and relies on surprise when hunting fish.

The eagle locates the fish from a perch or while soaring at between 200 and 300 m or gliding low over water. It may hover before plunging, but is not able to sustain a hover for very long. A favourite method seems to be to glide a few metres above the surface of the water: at the last moment the legs swing forward and the prey is grabbed from below the surface. Very occasionally it will plunge into the water. In shallow water the eagle will wade after fish, particularly where they are almost stranded in pools left by the outgoing tide. Fish account for about a third of the White-tailed Eagle's diet, but the proportions vary among individuals according to the availability of different types of food in different areas. Dr Willgohs, in a study of Norwegian eagles, reckoned an average daily consumption of something between 500 and 600 g. The usual weight of fish taken is 500 g to 3 kg, but one source claimed a 15-kg halibut as prey and there are several accounts of White-tailed Eagles being drowned when they attempted to take large Salmon or Halibut. An inability to take off with a large payload does not deter some eagles, and one was photographed in Greenland using its wings effectively to 'row' itself and its prey ashore.

The **Black Kite** is a very successful bird, whose range stretches across Europe and Asia to the Far East and south to the Cape and Australia. A large part of its success must be due to its wide choice of food and its boldness in taking it. It steals food from other birds and from human beings. A number of species of fish have been identified in the Black Kite's diet, which is perhaps not surprising as it shows a preference for rivers and lakes, particularly where there is human occupation. There is perhaps a link between the kite having learned early that human presence means good scavenging opportunities and the fact that human beings often settled near water. The fish it takes usually range in size from 12–20 cm, but may be as long as 30 cm; many are taken when dead or dying. The kite glides low over the water and snatches the fish in its claws in the same way as it snatches pieces of food from stalls in Indian bazaars. **Red Kites** have also been recorded taking fish in a similar manner from time to time.

Other species are occasionally reported carrying fish. In many cases the fish has probably been picked up as carrion. Sometimes, however, the fish is alive: Graham Madge saw a Buzzard carrying a live Eel, although he was unable to tell whether it had caught the Eel in water or as it was crossing damp ground.

EATING INVERTEBRATES

Although most raptors prey predominantly on vertebrates, many will eat some invertebrates and a few are specialist insect-eaters. The most specialized of the insect-eating raptors is the **Honey Buzzard**. It takes a range of insects of several orders which it digs from the ground with its powerful, scaly feet, the claws of which are only slightly curved and of equal length, which helps it to dig and to walk. Its nostrils are more slitted than those of other raptors and this may be to prevent blockage with earth and entrance by insects. Colonial insect species are particularly advantageous to Honey Buzzards, but many of these are stinging wasps and bees. To overcome this problem, the feet and legs are covered with thick scales and there are small, dense sting-proof feathers around the face. It is also possible that the Honey Buzzard has internal adaptations against venom, or some form of immunity.

Honey Buzzards locate their prey from flight or from a perch. In north-east France it was found that 85 per cent of the insects taken

The Honey Buzzard is well adapted to raid the nests of wasps and bees. Scaly feet, dense facial plumage and slit-like nostrils protect it from the insects's stings as it digs out their nests.

had been located in flight, the bird following insects to their nests. When searching, the Honey Buzzard will often perch on a low bush.

Wasp and bee nests are dug up using one foot or each foot alternately. Sometimes the bill is used, too. Digging may be quite vigorous, the bird reaching a depth of 40 cm until only the head is showing. This work wears down the claws.

Adult wasps are grasped by the abdomen and the sting nipped off before they are swallowed. In some instances it seems that wasps are killed only to remove them, the bird concentrating on the grubs in the nest. A diet so rich in insects is high in protein, and the Honey Buzzard may chew the cell walls of the wasp comb for roughage.

The Honey Buzzard hunts beetles and other insects on the ground, grasping them in its bill; it may cover up to half a kilometre on foot in search of insects. It will also catch flying insects, using its fine bill.

Black Kites hunt insects both on the ground and in flight, grasping them with their feet or their bill. Locusts and cockchafers are favourites among those taken in flight: grabbed with the foot, the head, thorax and wings removed and the abdomen devoured in mid-air.

ABOVE *Hunting on foot a Red Kite grabs an earthworm from a field. Females leave the nest early in the morning to go worming. When hunting worms and beetles, the Buzzard looks rather like a large thrush.* OPPOSITE *Insects form an important part of the diet of several smaller falcons and Levant Sparrowhawks. From the top: dark-phase Eleonora's Falcon, Hobby, Lesser Kestrel, Red-footed Falcon and Levant Sparrowhawk.*

The **Red Kite** is omnivorous, and hunts on foot for worms and beetles in hill pastures in mid Wales. It also flies in search of insects, gliding low over the fields. It appears that within this species individuals prefer certain types of food, such as invertebrates rather than vertebrates. Analysis of 169 pellets revealed that 21.6 per cent contained invertebrates, mainly beetles, but it was thought that a high proportion of these might have come from the crops of gulls on which the kites had been feeding. Females will leave the nest in the early morning to go worming. They also hunt for invertebrates in mild winters, taking earthworms, dung-beetles, caterpillars and spiders. In summer they will ccasionally hawk for flying butterflies and moths.

Worms and larger insects are hunted by **Buzzards** on the ground. The bird walks over the ground, catching worms and insects in its bill, and runs well, Colin Tubbs describing its short-run-pause-and-dart technique as 'almost thrush-like'. Buzzards have also been seen following the plough with gulls and crows, but they seem to be more suspicious, keeping at a distance of about 30 m from the machinery.

Unlike the other accipiters (Sparrowhawk and Goshawk), the **Levant Sparrowhawk** catches prey on the ground. Its prey is mainly large insects and small reptiles, caught on or near the ground from a slow flight at a height of 6–10 m, but it has been seen chasing cicadas from branch to branch in a tree.

Kestrels feed on insects, in addition to the vertebrates that make up three-quarters of their diet. Large insects, such as grasshoppers, are often taken in the same way as rodents on the ground, from the hover. The **Lesser Kestrel** feeds very largely on insects taken in flight and on the ground. Among the great variety of insects which it eats Coleoptera (beetles) and Orthoptera (grasshoppers and crickets) seem to be the orders mainly taken.

Lesser Kestrels hunt in loose flocks over open country, at 10–15 m above the ground, turning head-to-wind to hover briefly before continuing on another circle. Prey on the ground is swooped on. Flocks of Lesser Kestrels hawk for flying insects, taking them in their bills and eating them in the air. I have seen them using the thermals on a cliff face in the Judaean desert near Jericho, apparently hunting for flying insects. At night in towns, they will hunt flying insects attracted to street-lighting.

Another migrant falcon which takes insects in large numbers is the **Red-footed Falcon**, which breeds in eastern Europe and winters in southern Africa. Although the chicks are fed on small mammals, reptiles, frogs and birds, the adults are almost exclusively insect-eaters. Opportunists, they exploit seasonal and local abundance. Red-footed Falcons hawk after flying insects, and drop, shrike-like, from a look-out perch on those on the ground. The invention of the telegraph was a boon to Red-footed Falcons, and to birdwatchers, who know to watch the wires for these and other birds in eastern Europe.

Eleonora's Falcons delay their breeding season to coincide with the autumn crossing of the Mediterranean by migration-fat song-birds, but this tends to mask the fact that this bird feeds widely on insects at other times of the year. In early summer, they may be seen in flocks hawking above woods and scrub for beetles and other flying insects. I have watched a flock of 72 soaring on thermals on the Cycladean island of Andros, catching insects in their talons and transferring them to their bills. Like other hunters of flying insects they tend to be opportunists, taking whatever happens to be abundant at a particular time and in a particular place.

Another insect-eating falcon shares the Malagasy winter quarters with Eleonora's. The **Sooty Falcon** breeds in the deserts of north-east Africa and Israel, but not a great deal is known about either its detailed distribution or its behaviour. It has been recorded catching insects which were hovering around the branches of a low tree and it has been noted as being particularly active in the early morning and before dusk, but this may be because, like the Alpine Swift, it moves during the day to areas less accessible to people.

The dashing **Hobby** hunts high-flying birds and insects such as flying ants, moths and beetles, but it also takes dragonflies, which fly fast and low with considerable manoeuvrability. These it catches with its talons, then tears off their wings and transfers them to its bill. It often feeds on crepuscular insects such as chafers on summer evenings in southern England.

Steppe Eagles in Africa forage for termites and other insects between eight in the morning and four in the afternoon. An even more unlikely feeder on insects is the **Egyptian Vulture**, which will catch insects, snails and other invertebrates on the ground by following the plough. It will also catch insects in flight.

CARRION-EATERS

Many raptors will eat carrion, but it is the vultures that are the real specialists. The five species breeding in the region are found in the south. The main populations of one of them, the Lappet-faced Vulture, breed south of the Sahara, but a few Palearctic pairs may be found in Morocco and Mauritania (and until recently Israel). The other species are found around the Mediterranean and Black Seas and it is possible, in theory, to see all four species in the air at the same time in north-east Greece and parts of Turkey.

The **Griffon Vulture** roosts communally. In the morning, the vultures wait for the thermals and then begin to spiral upwards. They all depart in the same direction, and each individual appears to keep within sight of its neighbour so that it can react as soon as it sees its neighbour fly down to food. This is a technique of extensive flocking, enabling the birds to take advantage of the food-finding value of flocks and at the same time to cover an area up to a radius of 60 km from the nesting colony or roosting site.

When one vulture spots the movement of Magpies, crows and kites at a carcase, it glides down. The nearest vulture, perhaps 12 km away, will follow suit, as will its neighbour and so on throughout the flock. If you are in the vicinity, you will notice them moving in a much more positive manner than when they are soaring. Each alights some metres from the carcase and approaches timidly.

With its long, flexible neck the Griffon Vulture can reach into the body cavities of carcases of mammals as large as horses. The down on its head is sufficiently fine not to become matted with blood, and the edges of the bill sharp enough to sever chunks of soft meat quickly. The tongue has a series of sharp spines to help it to hold on to the more slippery contents of the carcase. Flesh or viscera may be anchored to the end of the bill and wrenched free. The skin may be torn open and the bones broken off for the flesh attached to them.

The vulture may carry a piece of the carcase several metres away before consuming it, but it is sometimes so greedy that it cannot take off. The much-travelled Meinertzhagen found one in Somalia that had become stuck within the carcase of a camel and he pulled it out by its tail. He also wrote of large numbers of Griffon Vultures being attracted by dead horses in the Franco-Prussian War of 1870–71, and recalled meeting a Crimean veteran who told him that hundreds of Griffon Vultures collected at Balaclava after the Charge of the Light Brigade: apparently, squads of soldiers were detailed to shoot them to protect the wounded. Soldiers during the Peninsular War in Spain at the beginning of the nineteenth century recorded crows, kites and eagles feeding on the dead after battles, and one particularly gruesome tale recounts the bodies of officers in the 95th regiment being dug up by wolves and their bones scattered across the ground by vultures. The species involved was not identified, but was almost certainly the Griffon Vulture.

About the same size as the Griffon Vulture is the **Black Vulture**. Its home range is less extensive. It does not fly so high when hunting, and it hunts in more wooded areas. While the Griffon flocks may contain as many as a hundred birds, the Black hunts on its own or in smaller groups which only rarely reach as many as forty.

The bulkiest of the European vultures, the Black is the dominant species at a kill. If one arrives at a carcase already being eaten by Griffons, it will shoulder them away. When it has finished, it will sit digesting its meal on a rock nearby. If it arrives before other birds at a carcase, the strength and sharpness of its bill enable it to break through the hide of an animal that would have to have rotted somewhat before the Griffon could tackle it. It can also tear through muscle tissue and tendons that are too tough for the Griffon.

While the Griffon eats virtually nothing but carrion, the Black Vulture will occasionally catch marmots, lizards and new-born lambs. Over a century ago, it was recorded as taking tortoises in Greece.

Griffon Vultures roost together, dispersing each day to travel long distances in search of carrion. These birds roosting at Monfragüe in Spain wait for the morning thermals to rise before taking to the air on their daily search for food.

A Black Kite flies down to a sheep's carcase being eaten by four Griffon Vultures. The smaller Egyptian Vulture in the foreground waits to make a dash to grab any morsels ignored by the Griffons. Magpies, a Red Kite and a Raven wait for an opportunity to eat.

Smallest of the European vultures is the **Egyptian Vulture**. It is much more catholic in its choice of food than the other vultures. In addition to carrion, it eats organic refuse of all types and will catch insects and reptiles. In Africa, it has been recorded eating the eggs of

pelicans and dropping stones on the eggs of Ostriches, behaviour that appears to be learned rather than innate.

The Egyptian has less need to soar than the other vultures and may be on the wing shortly after dawn. It spends much of the day soaring in search of food or perching near refuse tips and village rubbish dumps.

The other vultures and large eagles all dominate the Egyptian Vulture at a kill. The latter's comparatively weak bill can tear only softer tissues and it has to rely on opportunism, dashing in to grab

The Egyptian Vulture is an opportunist, taking both carrion and live food. One of its food items is birds' eggs, including those of White Pelicans and Ostriches, which it may crack open by dropping heavy stones on them.

soft scraps or stripping fragments of flesh from discarded bones. After the other vultures have left the carcase the Egyptian often stays to pick over the bones.

In Europe, the **Bearded Vulture** is the least likely of the vultures to form flocks. Each pair keeps to a home range with a radius of 6–8 km, but it may travel up to three times that distance on occasions. It lives in remote, mountainous districts. The Bearded Vulture's main food is carrion, but in competition with larger vultures it stands little chance. It specializes in eating marrow from bones which it splits open by dropping them from a height of 50–80 m on to rocks.

This vulture would win prizes for persistence: it may repeat the dropping twenty times. It lifts the bone in its feet, flies downwind above the rocks, drops the bone and turns head-to-wind and loses height rapidly. Tortoises and rock hyraxes have been seen to be dropped in the same way and with the same effect. Sheep, goats, chamois and men have been attacked by Bearded Vultures apparently trying to push them over the edge of a hill in an attempt to kill them. Human corpses have been among the carrion upon which Bearded Vultures have been seen to feed.

Several species of raptor, apart from vultures, will eat carrion when available. The **Black Kite** is a skilled scavenger, able to snatch

Bold and daring in search of food, the Black Kite has learned that the prsence of human beings means food and it will approach very close to people. In the Middle East and Africa, kites will snatch food from baskets and market stalls.

food from market stalls and from baskets being carried on people's heads. This is a dextrous bird, which will use its foot to hold down a carcase while it explores the body for wounds or openings into which it can insert its bill and tear. It feeds on muscles and fibres attached to bones and will pick up many smaller morsels ignored by vultures at a kill.

The **Red Kite** was once common across Britain and was renowned as a scavenger in the untidy streets of Tudor London. The relict population now existing in mid Wales is less dependent on carrion than its London ancestors and those on the Continent. Being less tolerant of human beings than the Black Kite, it does not scavenge so boldly, but carrion forms still an important proportion of its diet, particularly during the autumn.

To many birdwatchers, a Red Kite soaring in circles in search of food is one of the most beautiful sights in the bird world. When it spots carrion, the kite descends in ever-tighter circles to settle on the ground or a perch some distance from the food (when descending, the kite does not have its feet extended as it does when the prey is live). The kite will then walk up to the carrion or glide from the perch. Red Kites are not particularly bold and in Wales, when feeding on carrion, they will readily give way to Buzzards and even Ravens. They are not well equipped to break into the carcases of a large domestic animal and have to wait for other carrion-feeders to break through the skin.

In hard winters, **Buzzards** may find it difficult to catch small rodents beneath snow and they turn to birds as their main prey, but if numbers of small birds fall they may turn to carrion.

In northern Europe the White-tailed Eagle is the largest carrion-eater. On the shores of the Baltic a White-tailed Eagle uses its heavy bill to rip into the carcase of a Common Seal. Nearby, a Red Kite and a Buzzard wait for the eagle to finish before taking their turn.

To the north of the Mediterranean, the place of the vulture as a carrion-eater is taken to some extent by the larger eagles. Like the vultures, the **White-tailed Eagle** has broad, fingered wings which it uses for soaring on updraughts created by the winds in northern Europe, in search of prey which may be either dead or alive. Its large, sharp-edged bill is ideally adapted to tear into the carcasses of sheep, deer, seals and other mammals.

Analyses of the food taken by White-tailed Eagles in Norway shows them to be very catholic feeders, but it is not always possible to know what was killed and what was taken as carrion. The larger mammals and some of the larger birds were more probably taken as carrion, as would have been the fish that are normally found in deep water. Carrion seems to be eaten throughout the year, but it is most important, and most readily available, in winter.

In winter, carrion will form the bulk of the food of some **Golden Eagles**. Carcasses of domestic sheep and Red Deer are among the main sources in Scotland. Golden Eagles have, on occasion, been seen to catch and kill live lambs, but most of the lambs they take are probably dead. Large raptors with a wide-ranging diet are very often opportunists, making the most of whatever is available. There are geographical and local variations in availability, and food preference

The White-tailed Eagle is a pirate which will often take food from another predator. This one is trying to steal the Osprey's fish.

may also vary with individuals. For example, the **Spotted Eagle** in north-eastern Tatar eats mainly mammals, and takes carrion that is chiefly the carcases of sheep and horses, which are common because of the activities of poachers. Elks, dogs and goats are also among the carrion taken by this eagle.

PIRATES

The link between scavenging and piracy is close. If scavenging is taking food that is lying around, piracy is stealing food that has already been taken by another bird. Some raptors are habitual pirates. Others are opportunists, which see another bird with prey that they think might do for them.

The usual victims of **Black Kite** piracy, or kleptoparasitism, are other birds, but victims may include human beings. In India these kites will take food from tables, and there exist unauthenticated stories of their snatching food from the hands of al fresco diners. White-tailed Eagle, Sparrowhawk, Peregrine, Kestrel and Hobby have all been seen to drop food when chased by Black Kites. Herons, too, are chased until they disgorge their food.

The Hen Harrier and Short-eared Owl share the moorlands of northern Britain. Both hunt voles and here a harrier tries to steal the owl's prey.

Although sometimes the victim of the Black Kite, the **White-tailed Eagle** is a frequent kleptoparasite itself and among the list of species parasitized is the Black Kite. Although the raptors from which this eagle will steal food include Red Kite, Buzzard and Peregrine, the Osprey is the most frequently recorded victim. Other birds attacked include gulls, Snowy Owls, Ravens and Grey Herons. Regurgitating or dropping its prey is a safety device used by a bird that might itself fall prey to the eagle. Half-eaten fish will also be stolen from otters, which may be driven off by the eagle.

Piracy of food has not been recorded for the Steppe Eagle but it is not at all uncommon among **Tawny Eagles**, which will rob other raptors from the size of Kestrels to Bearded Vultures. These attacks begin high above the victim, which is dive-bombed with a series of barking cries and pursued closely until it drops its prey.

Kestrels are vulnerable to piracy from other raptors. Here, a Red-footed Falcon tries to steal a lizard from a female Kestrel.

Because they are relatively small and do not have the massive bill of large eagles **Kestrels** appear rather gentle by comparison, but they are also piratical if the opportunity occurs. Mike Everett watched a Kestrel steal a Short-tailed Vole from a Barn Owl. The owl was flying with the vole in its claws when the Kestrel flew beneath it, turned on its back and grabbed the vole with both talons; the owl flying at little more than 1 m from the ground, did not release the vole until it began to lose height and the 'wildly flapping Kestrel broke loose'. This would appear to demonstrate the Kestrel's great advantages in manoeuvrability. Kestrels have been seen to grab a Short-tailed Vole dropped by a Short-eared Owl that was being harried by two Carrion Crows and to take prey from Sparrowhawks and Merlins.

Kestrels are not immune to piratical attentions of other species. Raymond Hogg, watching several raptors hunting on the Tadten Plain in Austria, saw a female Kestrel on the ground with what appeared to be a small rodent. Suddenly a male **Red-footed Falcon** flew low across the field to land near the Kestrel, which he then knocked over with a blow. 'A scuffle ensued and the Kestrel made off without her prey, which the Red-footed Falcon secured. . .' Red-footed Falcons have also been seen robbing Lesser Kestrels.

Piracy within a species is not uncommon among colonial sea-birds, and **Eleonora's Falcons**, which live in loosely based colonies, will try to rob each other of food, especially if a falcon carrying food trespasses on the territory of another pair. One or both of the pair may attack and attempt to steal the prey. Cases of piracy among small falcons are probably exceptional. Most raptors are hunters, content to hunt or scavenge for their own food.

Raptors will also pirate prey from human beings. In addition to **Tawny Eagles** being attracted to shooting parties by gunshot and stealing wounded birds from sportsmen, there are several references to raptorial piracy. Meinertzhagen mentions an expedition to the Deccan in India when he shot an Alpine Swift, which fell to the ground 200 m away and was scooped up by a **Lesser Spotted Eagle** before he could retrieve it. He also recalls some twelve of this species perching in trees at Bharatpur, now a famous nature reserve but then a famous duck-shooting ground, waiting for the battue to begin.

CO-OPERATIVE HUNTING

Some species of raptor hunt in groups or pairs. None has developed co-operation in hunting to the degree that it is found in wolves, hunting dogs or lions, but none has such a complex social structure. In terms of finding food, the greatest number of individual raptors working together are those from colonies of **Griffon Vultures** which spread over many square kilometres in search of food, but always stay within sight of each other so that each sees when the next one descends to a carcase. The flocking of **Lesser Kestrels** and Eleonora's Falcons may have a food-finding value for these birds when they are feeding on flying insects, but these flocks may be no more than evidence of an abundance of food.

A pair of **Bonelli's Eagles** will hunt flocks of birds together, one keeping station above the other. The lower bird scatters the flock, separating and chasing an individual at which its mate then stoops. The victim is shared between the partners.

The closely related **Booted Eagle** also hunts in pairs. Very frequently both partners are to be seen in the air hunting at the same time, but they may also co-operate by flying at the same prey, stooping at it one after the other.

Co-operation between **White-tailed Eagles** can make the chase more effective. When hunting birds such as Eiders and divers, which can dive beneath the surface, a partner can double the chances of the prey surfacing within reach of an eagle. Working as a pair also increases the chances of spotting potential carrion.

Another large eagle that will hunt in pairs is the **Golden Eagle**. A herd of red deer will be harried by one bird, the other following at a distance of 100–200 m, ready to stoop on any fawn detached from the herd. Some of the reports of Golden Eagles hunting adult deer may be based on a mistaken interpretation of this hunting technique.

Sparrowhawks and Goshawks tend to hunt singly, but the **Levant Sparrowhawk**, a hunter of lizards and large insects that it catches on the ground, hunts in pairs outside the breeding season. Where insects are plentiful, there is an obvious advantage in two pairs of eyes.

Fast and dashing in its hunting, the **Merlin** does not drop dramatically from a height as do other falcons. Instead it flies low above heather and other bushes in pursuit of its avian prey. Almost a third of the observations of Merlins hunting involves the birds working in teams of two, usually a male and a female. Unlike other bird-catching falcons, the **Eleonora's Falcon** is rather sociable. It breeds in loose colonies on the rocky coasts of Mediterranean islands. When migrant songbirds cross the Mediterranean in late summer and early autumn, they have to pass through a barrage of Eleonora's Falcons hanging on the wind. A songbird that avoids one falcon may be chased by two or more. It is not clear whether these chases are competitive or co-operative, but Dr Walter, who interprets them as co-operative, qualifies the co-operation with the word 'selfish'.

The birds and mammals that are attracted to desert waterholes may cause the normally solitary **Lanner** to hunt in groups of up to twenty. While these hunt individually, pairs may hunt co-operatively, one falcon disturbing drinking birds and driving some towards the other, which then pounces unexpectedly.

Conditions along the steep cliffs of the west coasts of Britain are ideal for the co-operative hunting of a pair of **Peregrines**. Flocks of waders or pigeons can be seen at several kilometres' distance, which, if the wind is not too strong, gives the Peregrines plenty of time in which to prepare for the attack. The lighter male climbs steeply; the heavier female cannot climb so quickly, but she can fly faster. The male usually attacks first, relying on his altitude to give him speed; his stoop may scatter the flock giving the faster female the opportunity to select a victim and launch her attack. A pair of **Kestrels** hunting birds may employ similar tactics, with one scattering the birds in a flock in order that the other can pounce on an individual.

EATING PREY

Having caught their prey, raptors have to eat it. Even the sociable vultures may carry food a few metres away from the carcase. Other raptors feed on their own. Generally members of the family Accipitridae – hawks, buzzards and eagles – take their prey to a perch, where, if it is a bird, they pluck it and eat it whole. Mammals are plucked or torn in pieces, and smaller rodents are swallowed whole. The bones are normally digested, but fur, feathers, horny parts and chitin from the exoskeletons of insects are regurgitated as pellets.

The falcons eat their prey on the wing if it is small enough. Thus, insects and small birds, which are caught in the talons, are consumed in mid-air. Larger items are carried to a perch and, if not already killed by the falcon's talons, may be dispatched with a nip to the back of the neck. Birds and mammals are carefully plucked before being eaten. Large, hard bones and bills may be broken up before being swallowed. The pellets produced often consist only of feathers, fur, chitin from insects and, unlike with the Accipitridae, the feet and skulls of small birds.

As it consumes its prey a raptor is vulnerable to being robbed by another raptor or a corvid. To protect its food from other birds' opportunism it will spread its wings to cover the food. This is known as mantling and may also occur among young birds at the nest.

Pellets can be very useful indicators of a bird's diet if the identity of the species casting the pellets is known. The same applies to remains at a raptor's feeding place, but these can in themselves also be a clue to the raptor's identity.

It is not just raptors and owls that cast pellets of indigestible matter. Many other species do so. The basic shape of a bird pellet is cylindrical, but the length and the shape of the ends vary among species. With a length of up to 11 cm and a 4-cm diameter the **White-tailed Eagle's** is a giant among pellets, broad and solid with rounded ends. By contrast, the **Hobby** may cast a pellet as small as 2 cm long and 1 cm in diameter, with rounded ends and containing chitin from insects and the odd bird bone.

Remains at plucking posts may give you clues about the presence of raptors, but these are often no more than clues. Feathers plucked from the prey often blow away, leaving the inedible bits – the legs, wing-feathers and, in the case of larger birds, shoulder girdle. The **Sparrowhawk** plucks its prey on a hummock, stump or log, holding it down with one foot and tearing with its bill. **Peregrines** cope with their prey in a similar way, but tend towards larger birds. **Buzzards** which feed on mammals turn the carcases inside out.

COURTSHIP AND BREEDING

Raptors are at their most conspicuous when they are seeking a mate and establishing their breeding territories. As hunters, it is normally against their interests to be too obtrusive: their prey will take cover, or mob them, and man will all too often reach for his gun. When it comes to impressing a mate, to deterring rivals, and to laying a claim to a breeding territory, however, a raptor has to make itself obvious.

TIMING THE BREEDING CYCLE

Birds time their breeding cycles to ensure that there is the greatest chance of food being available when there are young in the nest to be fed. The postponement of breeding by **Eleonora's Falcons** until the second half of the summer is an extreme example of this: the young hatch when the greatest number of fat songbirds are moving south across the Mediterranean in late summer and early autumn.

The easiest prey for a bird-eating raptor is young fledglings that have left the nest but cannot yet fly strongly. For the individual bird this highly vulnerable stage lasts for no more than two weeks before its feathers grow and it can fly strongly. However, there are fledgling songbirds available throughout most of the summer, reaching a peak in Britain and Ireland between mid-May and mid-July depending on the latitude. For example, the breeding season of the **Sparrowhawk** is linked to the availability of fledgling songbirds: the period when the hawks have young in the nest coincides with the peak numbers of songbird fledglings.

For the large raptors the breeding cycle can be long and must start early. For **Griffon Vultures**, whose incubation lasts 52 days and whose fledging period may be 115 days, the season lasts from March to September. The **White-tailed Eagle's** courtship begins quite soon after the previous nesting season has ended, with some intermittent displays in October and November, increasing in intensity as early spring approaches. Except in the north of their range, White-tailed Eagles may well remain in their breeding territory throughout the year. The most northerly birds may be forced south by the freezing of the water where they hunt, but these migratory individuals move south in pairs and stay together to return in early March or April. The eagle's breeding range covers 35 degrees of latitude, from Turkey to Scandinavia: the White-tailed Eagle's breeding season may begin as early as January in the south of its range in Turkey, but not until as early May in northern Norway.

The migrant **Honey Buzzard** returns from sub-Saharan Africa in May and early June to take advantage of plentiful bees and wasps. This, particularly in the north of its range, is almost midsummer.

PAIR-BONDS

Once they have found a mate most raptors will maintain the pair-bond until the death of one of them, but monogamy is not so rigid that one of the pair may not be distracted by an intruder. In some migrant species, such as **Steppe Eagles**, the pair-bond, while monogamous for the breeding season, may not persist from year to year.

The pair-bond in **Ospreys** probably lasts longer than a season, encouraged by the birds' attachment to a particular nest-site. Alan Poole, working in New England, found that only five of 150 attempts at copulation involved what he described as 'divorced' birds, that is birds which had had a different mate the previous season, and where that mate still survived. In each case, the previous year's pairing had failed to produce young.

Ospreys return to their breeding grounds when the ice has broken up and the fish begin to move into the sun-warmed shallow water. Members of the pair do not migrate together. The males arrive a few days before the females: at the end of March or early April in Scotland, and a week or so later in April in Sweden. Experienced birds waste no time: eggs are laid about ten days after their return. Younger birds take longer to get started and may have to construct a nest from scratch, which can mean that they do not lay for thirty days. One reason for the delay among young birds may be the reluctance of young males to feed females, which appears to be the trigger that stimulates copulation.

Despite strong monogamous pair-bonds, some birds of prey do occasionally mate with individuals that are not their 'regular' mates. This is opportunistic and exceptional. It would be easy to draw parallels with human pair-bonding, but so far as birds are concerned, the reasons for fidelity are practical. The pair-bond in raptors must be maintained to ensure that a female has a mate who can provide her with food when she is incubating and for her chicks when they have hatched and for the male, the female's fidelity ensures that it his sperms that fertilize the female's eggs, thereby ensuring the survival of his genes.

The smaller raptors seem to be less likely to remain monogamous for more than a season. Ian Newton, from his extensive study of

Sparrowhawks, concludes that the fidelity from season to season is associated with fidelity to territory. Thus, a male who changes territory will probably change mates. The female may go to the new territory with him, move off to a new mate and a new territory or stay put and take on a new mate.

Nesting colonially, **Lesser Kestrels** must have strong pair-bonding if they are to remain monogamous throughout their nine-week breeding season. Hunters of insects and reptiles, they are summer migrants, moving south from the Mediterranean and Middle East to winter in sub-Saharan Africa. They begin to arrive back in their Mediterranean breeding sites in mid-March. Males arrive first and select their own nest-sites among the holes and crevices in cliff faces where the colony nests. A few days later the females arrive.

After their breeding season has finished, **Kestrels** may maintain their bond into the autumn. If the pair stays in its breeding territory, it will probably retain the bond into the next breeding season. Pairs that disperse may come back together the following spring. Some birds may maintain a pair-bond for several years.

The mortality rate of raptors, while lower than that of their prey species, is still high. For example, among **Peregrines,** whose pair-bonds last from year to year, there is an annual mortality of between a quarter and two-thirds among those birds that have survived their first year. If one of a pair dies, its mate may find a replacement within a few hours, but it may take weeks or even not until the next breeding season. How quickly a replacement is found depends on the stage which the breeding cycle has reached. In the early years of the twentieth century, John Walpole-Bond recorded one female who had three successive new mates during one March: as well as evidence of her tenacity, it was a comment on the frequency with which the Peregrine was persecuted by man. One female, who lost her mate during the incubation stage, managed to obtain a new mate who supplied her with food and helped to rear her brood.

DISPLAYS

Any bird holding a territory needs to make other members of the same species aware of the fact; if it is unpaired, it is also in search of a mate. Therefore, the initial reason for the display is to advertise its territory-holding in order to warn off other males and to attract a potential mate. Once the mate has been chosen, the pair displays together to reaffirm the bond.

Among the eagles, hawks and vultures, the Accipitriformes, there are three basic types of display – perching-and-calling, soaring-and-calling, and mutual aerial displays. The parents' hunting skill is a key to the survival of the young raptors in the nest. The bulk of the hunting during the nestling period is the responsibility of the male, so that a female seeks a mate which is good provider, and much of the courtship is a demonstration of flying and hunting skills.

Perching-and-calling is common to many species of raptor and usually takes place in the vicinity of the nest. Among woodland species, therefore, it is rarely witnessed by the birdwatcher, but it can be quite obvious among larger raptors such as the **White-tailed Eagle**. One of the pair, usually the male, will perch near the nest, calling with his head thrown back and bill sky-pointing and the wings held partially open.

The most frequent and widespread aerial display is soaring-and-calling. **Sparrowhawks** will do this above the woodland in which they are nesting. They may display in this way at any time, but favour bright and breezy mornings in particular. They soar singly or sometimes as a pair, displaying the white patches below the tail. Paired **White-tailed Eagles** will fly together, soaring-and-calling, and may then follow each other up to 6-m apart or spiral in opposite directions. **Griffon Vultures** fly side-by-side in pairs in slow circles, their wingtips almost touching.

The display of White-tailed Eagles is dramatic. The pair will fly together, soaring and calling, then swooping at each other and cartwheeling through the air with clasped talons.

Egyptian Vultures perform spectacular displays including dives and steep climbs, rolls and talon presentation. Occasionally two birds will approach close enough to clasp talons.

It is the mutual aerial displays that produce the most dramatic flying. They are often a modification of aggressive display and may involve one bird swooping at its partner in mock attack. Such display is at its most striking among **White-tailed Eagles**. One bird will swoop at the other, which turns over to present its talons, linking them to those of the top bird. With talons thus linked, the pair then tumbles or cartwheels through the air, disengaging when they have to within a few metres of the ground or sea. Similar talon-clasping has been recorded for kites and may occur occasionally in other species such as **Griffon Vultures**.

Many species sky-dance. The well-watched **Osprey** performs a sky-dance, which is sometimes called a 'fish-flight'. The male flies overhead, its flight slow, high and undulating, and uttering a penetrating, rhythmic trisyllabic call. Often a fish hangs from its talons, but a stick or other item of nest material may be substituted for the fish or the bird may merely dangle its legs as if it were carrying something. A paired male may perform this dance early in the courtship, but more often this display is performed by unpaired males, which have to work much harder in advertising for a mate. Ospreys do not spend very much time in display, preferring, it seems, to concentrate on the more essential business of feeding and mating.

Bonelli's Eagles perform very active displays which involve being on the wing for long periods. They fly fast over the woods where they are nesting, in loops and other evolutions, either in pairs or singly. When the eagle high-circles in tight spirals, it reaches up to

Bonelli's Eagles have very active displays which include flying high over the nesting wood and performing high-circling and sky-dancing. This bird is climbing as part of its sky-dance.

*A sky-dancing Booted Eagle plunges steeply with wingtips held
close to its tail, creating a characteristic 'W'-shape. This dance is
accompanied by calls and consists of steep undulations.*

800 m above the wood. As it circles, it throws itself from side to side
before plummeting steeply on still wings held stiffly behind its body.
It checks at the foot of the descent before beginning a steep climb from
which it loops the loop. When it is almost flying upside-down it drops,
calling. This performance may be repeated for up to half an hour.

The virtuosity of **Peregrines** as fliers is amply demonstrated in the
displays in their nesting territories. Before flying out of his territory in
the evening the male will high-circle for from ten to twenty minutes.
He may come out of the high-circling by descending steeply, levelling
off again, descending steeply in the opposite direction, levelling off,
repeating this so-called 'Z-flight' until returning to the cliff face or
high-circling again.

Another Peregrine display involves one of the pair, usually the
male, leaving the nest-site and performing a tight figure-of-eight
circuit in a level plane, almost brushing the cliff with its belly as
it turns. The birds will then high-circle together, and this display
often turns into mutual flight-play with the two chasing each other,
swooping and diving. They fly directly at each other, turning away
at the last moment. Sometimes they delay the turn until they appear
to touch bill-to-bill or breast-to-breast.

A sky-dancing male Hen Harrier climbs steeply to about 30 m before somersaulting into a steep dive and climbing again. It may take twenty or more undulations or as few as three.

The harriers excel as sky-dancers. In Scotland, the most intense aerial display among **Hen Harriers** is in mid April. The grey male climbs steeply to about 30 m, rolls or somersaults, dives steeply, to above the ground and starts to climb again. The late Eddie Balfour, the Orcadian Hen Harrier expert, recorded one bird performing 105 successive dives. The sky-dancers are often males which have lost mates, but may be young unpaired males in search of a mate. Sky-dancing is at its most intense among pairs nesting close together, and both partners may very rarely sky-dance together. If Hen Harrier nests are a few kilometres apart, the sky-dance rarely takes place.

For several species of raptor, courtship feeding is an integral part of establishing the pair-bond. It is exciting to watch, especially if the food is passed in the air. In many cases, though, food is presented by the male to the female at the nest or a nearby perch. The male **Sparrowhawk** brings food, usually plucked, to the female, perches, calling softly and holding the food in one claw. She flies directly at him, and at the last moment he releases the food on the perch and flies away. Sometimes the male brings food to the nest area, hovers briefly a few metres from the ground with the food held in one talon, and drops it to the female to grab as she swoops beneath him.

*Courtship feeding is an integral feature in establishing the pair-bond
in many raptors. The male presents the female with an item of food.
This may be placed on a parch or at the nest for the female to take,
as is the case with the Black Kite (above), or, as with Marsh Harriers
(opposite), the flying male may drop the prey to be caught by the
female flying below him.*

The aerial food-pass is a feature of the displays of harriers. As well
as helping to maintain the pair-bond, it is a practical way of transferring food, particularly when the birds nest in long vegetation.
Among **Marsh Harriers**, courtship feeding develops into provisioning
the female during incubation and the early stages of brooding. Thus,
for about sixty days from early spring it is possible to see the Marsh
Harrier's food-pass. The male approaches with the food dangling
from his talons. Usually he flies at between 10 and 30 m, summoning
the female from the nest with a food-call. The female may call in
response and fly up to meet her mate, flying below and slightly
behind him. He drops the prey, which she catches in her own talons
by twisting in mid-air. If it is windy or the prey item is small, the
female will take the food directly from the talons of her mate.

All the other harriers and several other species of raptor will pass food in the air. The male **Peregrine** drops food to the female in flight. The female turns and grabs the food in her talons, but sometimes approaches close enough to take the food from the male's talons. Occasionally the male will pass food bill-to-bill in flight, but this is more usual as part of the courtship feeding that takes place on a ledge.

Like other large falcons, the Peregrine is solitary and aggressive to other Peregrines outside the breeding season. In its courtship display it must communicate that its aggression has been suspended in the case of its mate. Even when a pair has stayed loosely together during the winter they repeat the same courtship each spring. In the air the male appears to be dominant, but on the breeding ledge it is the larger female who dominates.

Peregrine courtship may begin in the autumn, when the young have gone, and continue in a rather desultory way throughout the winter. More usually it is on mild sunny days that the female's interest in her old nest-sites is aroused. She will visit the eyrie in the mornings and evenings, and the male will wail and stoop at her. The pair may quietly perch on the same cliff face, gradually moving nearer to each other as the pair-bond develops over successive days.

One bird will sit on the edge of the nest-ledge calling. When its mate arrives, the two call together with their heads lowered below the level of the body to indicate lack of aggression. Each of the pair performs its own ledge-display, the male's being more elaborate than the female's. These displays develop into a mutual display. The male approaches a scrape on the ledge (but not necessarily the nest-scrape) with a high-stepping swagger, giving a creaky call. In the scrape he bows and turns for five to ten seconds, calling continuously, pausing for the female's reaction. If she moves towards him, he continues his activity. The female's ledge-display is less active. When the display becomes mutual there is great activity around the scrape.

CHOOSING A NEST-SITE

Most species of raptor nest at a considerable distance from the next pair, maintaining a home range large enough to provide food for their brood without the competition from other individuals of the same species. Some, however, are colonial. These are species for whom flocking has an advantage in food-finding, and their prey tends to be carrion or insects. The sites for colonies tend to be traditional, in use from year to year.

Griffon Vultures nest in colonies in which there are usually fifteen to twenty pairs, but there may be as many as one hundred pairs or as few as five. Each nest is on a cliff ledge and is protected by an overhang. The ledge has to have enough space for a nest that can have a diameter of up to 1 m.

Lesser Kestrels and **Red-footed Falcons** are both colonial nesters. Lesser Kestrels show a preference for towns, choosing to nest in holes on tall buildings, churches, mosques or old walls. Occasionally they will nest in holes in cliffs. Colonies are usually not large, between fifteen and twenty pairs, although up to one hundred have been recorded. Male Lesser Kestrels arrive at the colonies before the

Male Lesser Kestrels, which arrive at colonies before the females, choose the nest-sites. Carrying an item of prey, in this case a lizard, the male flies back and forth to attracts a mate to his chosen site.

females and immediately start to prospect for nest-sites. The site will have been chosen by the time the female arrives. To advertise his site the male flies among the flock wheeling above the colony, calling and carrying in his talons a lizard as he flies up and down in front of it. He will chase the female and lead her to the nest-site. Courtship feeding begins the moment the female is shown the nest-site.

Red-footed Falcons are usually colonial, and there may be up to two hundred pairs in a colony. The falcons choose to nest in the disused nests of Rooks. This may mean nesting in an active rookery and occupying disused nests on the periphery.

Peregrines and **Golden Eagles** also use traditional sites: some of today's Peregrine sites were recorded as being in use in the twelfth century. Peregrines choose ledges on inland cliffs and sea-cliffs, and increasingly on office-buildings and churches. Although sites are often traditional, Peregrines may have a choice of up to five sites within their territories. These may be more than 6 km apart. The ledge must be at least 45 cm deep and either be soft enough to create a shallow scrape or contain the remains of another bird's nest.

Perhaps because they are so large and have caught the imagination of people for so many years, the traditional nest-sites of **White-tailed Eagles** have been well recorded. An eyrie on the basalt cliffs of the Shiant Islands in the Outer Hebrides was mentioned by Martin Martin in his *Description of the Western Isles of Scotland*, published in 1716. The last occupants of this eyrie were shot by a collector in the early years of this century.

Occasionally **Golden Eagles** nest in large trees, but more usually they choose wide cliff ledges. Sometimes the nest may be built against a bush or small tree to provide shade. The preferred site is high, with a commanding view of the surrounding moorland.

Unusually among raptors, **Sparrowhawks** build a new nest each year, often in a new site. They prefer to build in conifers, placing their nests against the trunk on branches on the south side of the tree. Until larch and spruce were widely planted during this century Sparrowhawks nested in hardwoods, but now they seem to choose conifers in preference to their traditional trees. Presumably, as the population of Sparrowhawks has increased, a greater proportion will be nesting in hardwoods. When choosing where to nest the male flies around potential sites, watched by the female. Either bird may then break off and carry a twig from site to site. Twigs are placed on branches at each site. This seems to be a type of testing, and if the twig falls to the ground that site appears to be eliminated. The birds may pile twigs in a number of sites before concentrating on one.

Throughout the world **Ospreys** use a variety of sites, but northern birds prefer to use trees, although a famous traditional Scottish site no longer in use was a ruined castle on an island in Loch-an-Eilean. The Osprey seems to have three criteria for site selection. As an almost exclusive eater of fish it must nest near water, which in the case of the strong-flying Osprey means anything up to 5 km away. The access to the nest must be open to accommodate the bird's long wings, which explains this species' choice of flat-topped conifers. It also needs to be safe from interference by predators, such as Pine

Martens, which means nesting as high as possible. On the island of Tiran in the Gulf of Aqaba there are no mammalian predators, and a colony of about thirty pairs nests on the ground. At another maritime site on the coast of Corsica, they nest on cliffs and pinnacles of rock.

In the United States Ospreys nest on a variety of man-made structures, especially when, like channel-markers and pierheads, they are surrounded by water. They also take to well-placed, deliberately created artificial sites such as wagon wheels placed on the tops of poles. In northern Germany Ospreys display a similar preference for artificial sites: over 50 per cent in Mecklenburg and Brandenburg nest on artificial sites, mainly electricity pylons.

The provision of nestboxes for **Kestrels** in the open, treeless Dutch polders has encouraged a healthy population which feeds on the plentiful voles that have been quick to exploit newly created farmland. A nesting platform was built on the roof of a British Telecom building in Swansea to encourage **Peregrines**. It was successful, but when the young left the nest there were no nearby ledges on which they could rest and they floated down to the street below, surprising passing pedestrians and the driver on whose car bonnet one is said to have landed. Fortunately they survived this, and the next year the nesting ledge was moved to the top of a lift shaft, allowing the young to spread their wings above the safety of the roof.

BUILDING A NEST

Some raptors, such as Ospreys, seem to be compulsive nest-builders, adding each year to their nests. Others such as Peregrines make do with rudimentary scrapes in the earth. Several raptors use the cast-offs of other species: the old nests of corvids seem to be particularly favoured, presumably because the original owners build structures of substance and move to new premises each year.

Using the same nests from year to year and adding more sticks annually, **Ospreys** can build very large structures. Winter winds in northern areas may mean that some of the sticks from the nest fall to the ground, but both birds of the pair add material to the nest during the pre-laying period. The male brings the material, sometimes almost as long as the bird itself, and the female does the building. At first twigs and branches broken from trees are dropped on the nest. A sure sign that egg-laying is imminent is the birds bringing in weeds, grass and seaweeds with which to line the nest: the species' recently-acquired penchant for plastic bags and fishing line as lining material can have fatal consequences for the young. Although the average diameter of an Osprey's nest is about 150 cm and the depth about 60 cm, some of the older nests are very much larger.

ABOVE *A pair of Buzzards may have as many as fifteen nests between which they change from year to year. The nests are large and this male is bringing an additional branch as part of its courtship.* OPPOSITE *Nests of raptors. Top to bottom and left to right: Peregrines make a scrape on a cliff ledge, whereas the Hobby makes use of a crow's old nest. The Griffon Vulture requires an overhang beneath which to build its large nest and the Sparrowhawk builds its nest on a branch close to the main trunk. The Golden Eagle uses a traditional nest to which it adds more material each year and the tree-top nests of Ospreys are similarly added to each year, producing enormous structures.*

The greatest variety of nest types is demonstrated by the **White-tailed Eagle,** whose nest may be anything from a simple scrape in the ground to a massive collection of sticks. These huge structures can reach up to 3 m in depth and represent years of sticks being added. As if to prove their nesting versatility, some White-tailed Eagles will usurp the nest of other birds and have been known to evict both Ospreys and Red Kites.

Where the raptor nests on the ground, the nest is rarely more than a scrape in the earth. **Hen Harriers**, however, do build rough nests on the ground, having collected material from within 200 m of the site. From his observations of nesting Hen Harriers, Donald Watson suggests that the females become better nest-builders as they gain experience from year to year. The **Marsh Harrier**, nesting in reedmarsh, needs a substantial structure to keep its eggs and young dry. The female makes a nest with a diameter of 50–80 cm that is a pile of grass, reeds and small sticks. Usually it is about 30 cm high, but is taller in very wet areas; as the breeding season progresses, the mound becomes flattened with use.

Buzzards build large nests with an average diameter of 1 m and, like many species of the family Accipitridae, they decorate it with greenery. No one is sure what function these leafy branches perform, but they may play a part in concealing the young and the nest. So much greenery is collected by some **Honey Buzzards** that their nests appear to be completely green and are difficult to see.

In contrast to other raptors, the nests of falcons are rudimentary: either scrapes in the earth or disused nests of other birds. While **Lesser Kestrels** make a scrape in holes in buildings, **Kestrels** will either use an old nest or make a shallow scrape in a tree-hole or, where no trees are available, in a rabbit-burrow. **Merlins** are also versatile in that some will nest on the ground and others use old nests in trees.

MATING

Copulation for most birds is brief. The female stands and her mate balances on her back, using his wings to steady himself. Each bird moves its tail sideways and the feathers are displaced around the cloaca of each. The contact must be long enough for their cloaca to be brought together and the sperm to pass from male to female.

In many species, copulation does not occur very frequently; when a male constantly guards his mate against the attentions of other males he needs only a low copulation rate to ensure that it is his sperms that fertilize her eggs, thus females of some, such as the Skylark, copulate only once per clutch.

On the other hand, in species where females are vulnerable to extra-pair attentions of males, their mates have to copulate with them frequently to increase the probability that it is their own sperms that fertilize the eggs. This need is greatest among polyandrous species and those where the males are unable to guard their mates without interruption. The most frequent copulators are among those raptor species in which the males leave their mates while they forage for food. To minimize the risk of cuckoldry, the male must attend his mate and copulate with her as often as he can, because it increases the number of his sperms delivered to his mate. **Goshawks** average between five and six hundred copulations per clutch. The female is most likely to be fertilized just after she has laid an egg because the sperm can travel up an unobstructed oviduct within fifteen minutes. This is called by T.R. Birkhead and A.P. Møller the 'insemination window', and occurs for Goshawks in the early morning and during the laying period males are scrupulous in their attendance at this time of day.

To discover such detailed information about the sex-lives of birds requires constant monitoring of nests and it is not surprising that it exists for few species. However, the intensive watching of the Loch Garten **Ospreys** suggests that the male minimizes the risk of cuckoldry by spending 70 per cent of the day with his mate at the onset of egg-laying. The average number of copulations per clutch was 59, beginning with the female's spring-time arrival in the territory some two weeks before egg-laying. As egg-laying approaches, the male spends an increasing amount of time at the nest, but must still catch the food needed by his mate during this period.

EGGS AND EGG-LAYING

The demise (but not total disappearance) of egg-collecting has led to a diminution of knowledge about eggs among birdwatchers. Few of us have seen raptor eggs in the nest, which for the sake of the survival of birds of prey is good. Apart from any threat from those remaining anachronisms – people who still collect eggs – raptors' eggs may be in danger from the attentions of other predators.

Raptors' eggs are attractively patterned, and this, together with the relative rarity of the birds and the willingness of gamekeepers to allow egg-collectors to take the eggs of birds that they saw as competitors, meant that the collectors did serious damage to raptor populations in Britain and Ireland in the first part of this century. But to look through an egg-cabinet at the results of their depredations is to understand the attraction of the eggs to the collector. They are beautiful – white or pale cream, blotched with browns and oranges. In the dappled shade of woodland the blotches break up the outline and camouflage it from predators when the adult is not sitting.

Usually the eggs of ground-nesting birds are well camouflaged, but the harriers lay white or greenish eggs and rely on the female sitting tight. **Hen Harriers'** eggs are left very briefly a couple of times a day when the male calls the female off the nest for the food-pass.

The blotching on an egg occurs as it moves down the oviduct. There may be variation among individual eggs in a clutch and between the eggs of individual birds. **Golden Eagle** eggs vary from well marked to almost unmarked, and as the females become older they may lay paler or unmarked eggs.

Generally, the eggs of raptors are more rounded than ovate, but as the markings of raptor eggs can vary, so can their size and shape.

The ratio of the weight of an egg to the weight of the female is higher among smaller raptors than among larger ones. The weight of a **Sparrowhawk's** egg is about 8 per cent of the female's weight, compared with 4 per cent in the case of the **White-tailed Eagle**. Corresponding percentages in falcons are 10 per cent for the small **Red-footed Falcon** and 5 per cent for the **Gyrfalcon**.

Three nestling Rough-legged Buzzards show the effect of asynchronous hatching, with the eldest six days older than the youngest. This ensures the greatest chance of survival for the eldest if the food supply fails.

Clutch size also shows a relationship to the size of the bird. The larger the bird, the fewer eggs it lays in a clutch. Thus, the large vultures lay a single egg, eagles and sea eagles two, kites and some buzzards two or three, and the Sparrowhawk three to six in the north of its range but two to six in the Mediterranean region. Harriers lay four to six eggs: as ground-nesters they may be more vulnerable to

Female Kestrels take the greatest share of the incubation, although they may leave the nest to feed. This male brings food to his incubating mate.

predation than other raptors. There may also be a relationship between clutch size and prey taken. The **Honey Buzzard** lays two eggs, while the similarly sized **Buzzard** lays up to four. Bird-eating species tend to lay smaller clutches than the mammal-eaters: among the falcons, the **Hobby**, which eats insects and birds, lays two or three eggs, while the **Kestrel** lays from three to six, or up to nine.

Availability of food may influence the clutch size of some raptors. Rodent populations fluctuate markedly: increases in lemming numbers are part of natural history lore, but voles are similarly affected. In the northern tundra these fluctuations occur in approximately four-year cycles. When rodent numbers are high the **Rough-legged Buzzard** lays up to seven eggs, but when they are low it may only lay two.

INCUBATION

The breeding season of raptors is lengthy and, therefore, the young birds, almost helpless in the nest, are at risk. Many raptors hedge against these risks by adopting a strategy that leads to asynchronous hatching. Among passerines and some smaller birds of prey, the female lays eggs at daily intervals, but does not begin to incubate them until the last egg has been laid. This means that the eggs all hatch within a few hours of each other. Many raptors, however, begin to incubate after the first egg has been laid. If the eggs are laid at two-day intervals, the first to hatch of a four-egg clutch will be six days old when the last egg hatches. This nestling has an advantage over its siblings, beginning with two days of food for which there have been no rivals. Conversely the youngest is at a disadvantage, and if there is a food shortage will almost certainly die and may even be eaten by a hungry brother or sister. If all had hatched at the same time, however, none might have survived.

Sparrowhawks do not start to incubate until the last egg is laid, which means that the young hatch synchronously. Because the females are larger than the males, there is a danger that in the nest they might turn on their smaller brothers. While the females gain weight faster, the males' plumage and behavioural development is more rapid and they fly at 26 days, about four days before the females.

For raptors the incubation period varies enormously, lasting for from little more than three weeks to almost eight weeks depending on the species. The small **Red-footed Falcon** incubates for only 22 or 23 days, while the incubation period of the **Black Vulture** is 55 days.

Eggs are vulnerable to the large feet and sharp talons of raptors, and an incubating eagle shows surprising delicacy as it clenches its claws to avoid crushing the eggs.

Honey Buzzards and **Griffon Vultures** demonstrate equality of work when they incubate, but in many species the female alone incubates. Occasionally the male will cover the eggs during the female's short absences. In April, when **Kestrels** are incubating, those females seen hunting during the day are young and unpaired birds; breeding females appear in the early evening. Among others both parents share the chore, but the female takes the lion's share, usually sitting throughout the night. As hatching approaches, the female becomes reluctant to leave the nest at all, even to hand over to the male.

In the case of **Sparrowhawks**, the young begin to chip at the eggshell up to 48 hours before hatching. Female Sparrowhawks and harriers may moult while incubating.

REARING CHICKS

With chicks in the nest for a month or two, the parents must show a high degree of parental care in feeding, brooding and sheltering the young before they fledge.

When the eggs hatch the female removes the eggshells, eats them or tramples them into the nest. She still does not move far from the nest. For the first few days she broods the young, still relying on the male to bring in food. He has to step up his production rate, and this is his busiest period. A male **Sparrowhawk** makes three kills a day during incubation, but once the young have hatched the average will increase to a daily 6.5. Young **Red-footed Falcons** consume almost their own weight in frogs and large insects each day, while the adults take a third of their own weight.

Although he rarely incubates, the male **Golden Eagle** shares the brooding of the young, bringing food which his mate tears up and feeds to the young bill-to-bill. If the female raptor is brooding, the male will arrive at a perch nearby with food and call his mate off the nest. In the case of harriers, this feeding takes the form of a food-pass in mid-air. Males of some species will bring food directly to the nest for the female to feed to the young. Male **Sparrowhawks** usually pluck and decapitate their prey before bringing it to the nest or to a nearby perch.

As the natal down of the chicks is replaced with their pale down, the female's instinct to kill returns. This is not always gradual: a female **Golden Eagle**, who has not hunted for several weeks of incubation and brooding, may abruptly leave the nest in pursuit of a distant rabbit. For most raptors, the period of brooding by the female is between seven and fourteen days. During this time, and even when she is not actually brooding, she stays close to the nest, where she can see off predators, can shelter the young from sun and rain and, in the case of some Accipitriformes, may decorate the nest with greenery, the full purpose of which is not yet understood.

The female's return to hunting relieves the male, which may no longer visit the nest, but will pass food to the female away from the nest. As the young approach fledging, the parents provide less food.

Differences in ages of the young that have hatched asynchronously can cause 'Cain and Abel' battles. These battles occur in the nests of **Golden Eagles**, **Buzzards** and **Lesser Spotted Eagles**. The elder chick will attack the younger and eight times in ten will succeed in destroying it or throwing it out of the nest. With Golden Eagles these attacks usually begin soon after the younger has hatched. Although the smaller sibling may fight back, it soon accepts its elder sibling's dominance and will retreat to the edge of the nest. Attacks persist, particularly when food is brought to the nest. The elder pursues the younger around the nest and will stab at its head, neck and back. It may also grab its sibling and throw it in the air.

Because these attacks take place when the birds are being fed, the adults are often present, but they never interfere or show any concern. Indeed, once the younger nestling is dead, the adult may eat it or feed it to the other. For **Golden Eagles**, the younger bird's chances of survival are better if it is a female. Leslie Brown calculated the

survival rate of younger siblings to be 20 per cent. If they survive until they are feathered, at about eight weeks, they seem to be safe, because no attacks have been seen after this stage; the siblings may, however, nibble at each other's bills and toes. Among **Lesser Spotted Eagles**, the younger chick never survives unless the elder is lost.

The significance of the Cain and Abel battles has been the source of great debate. Since the death of the younger is four times as likely as its survival, it is difficult to accept the theory that this behaviour is linked with food shortages. Another not entirely satisfactory view is that the second chick provides insurance against the accidental loss of the elder. This reasoning has been applied to the habit of certain boobies of laying two eggs but rearing only one young, but the circumstances of colonial boobies are very different from those of solitary raptors.

DEVELOPMENT IN THE NEST

The age of the young can be estimated with some accuracy from their plumage development. Although the periods of each stage of development vary among species, the stages themselves are similar for all raptors.

When raptor chicks hatch they are what is known as semi-altricial, hardly able to move and covered in a sparse white down. They are weak, their floppy appearance exaggerated by their heavy heads. Like human babies they are helpless. They may not be able to stand for some days, resting instead on their 'haunches'. Once the female begins to feed them they grow rapidly. The rate of growth is fastest in the early stages, but a chick becomes at least fifty times its hatching weight by the time the fledging is complete. At first they must be fed frequently.

The fine first down gives way to thicker, woollier and often darker down. This happens at seven to ten days in **Red-footed Falcons**, ten to twelve days in **Ospreys** and at about twenty days in the **White-tailed Eagle**. At about this time the chicks become mobile enough to stagger to the edge of the nest and defecate horizontally to clear the nest. In trees this results in leaves and branches below the nest becoming whitened by droppings, but at cliff sites the blanching is on the rocks at and above the nest.

The development of a Kestrel. From the bottom: covered with fine down at a day old; covered in darker, thicker down at ten days; contour feathers begin to appear between fourteen and eighteen days; its flight and tail feathers have emerged at 23–25 days; and the bird is fully fledged at about 34 days. It takes at least 28 days more to become fully independent.

True feathers begin to appear about a third of the way through the fledging period. In most species the first to grow are primaries and tail feathers, but some begin with the head feathers.

Once feathered, the young are left to themselves by the parents except when food is brought. By the time they are halfway through fledging the chicks can usually feed themselves instead of being fed bill-to-bill. When the parents bring food for fledged young, the young bird no longer falls flat and begs: it grabs the prey and mantles it with its wings to prevent the others getting it. The young are now as large as their parents, and the latter, faced with their offspring's aggressive postures, stay at the nest no longer than is necessary.

Left to themselves, chicks will examine their immediate environment, picking up and playing with sticks and remnants of prey. They watch with intensity the movements of insects on branches, birds in neighbouring trees and animals passing beneath the nest. They build their muscles by flapping their wings and will venture from the nest along branches or neighbouring rocks. It seems that male chicks, particularly among species in which the females are larger, develop sooner, are more active and wander further from the nest and flap their wings more vigorously. Wing-flapping, which will often become more intense as the time of leaving the nest approaches, may be less frequent in some species than in others, and there are variations among individual birds.

While wing-flapping, the young bird may lift off vertically like a helicopter. Maybe for this reason the first flight is usually on a day when there is wind; it is not usually far, and the bird will reach a nearby perch.

The length of the fledging period – from hatching to first flight – varies greatly. For the smaller falcons it is 25–32 days, compared with seventy to eighty days for **Golden Eagles** and up to 115 days for **Griffon Vultures**, whose young may leave the nest to wander short distances and back at eighty to ninety days.

Because flight is so important to a raptor's hunting, the young are unable to feed themselves until they are proficient fliers. They remain, therefore, dependent for food on their parents for days or even weeks. **Red-footed Falcons** are independent within a week or ten days of leaving the nest. **Kestrels** take four weeks and **Peregrines** up to six weeks. The larger the raptor the longer the dependence appears to be, but because the birds range widely it is not always possible to know the length of the period of dependence with any accuracy. Young **Golden Eagles** in Scotland stay with their parents for up to three months, but dependence is certainly shorter for migrant populations. **Griffon Vultures**, on the other hand, are able to feed themselves soon after they can fly, because they do not have to hunt live prey to survive.

Young bird-eating raptors will chase potential prey, but not, it seems, with the intention of catching it as, **Sparrowhawks** at least, do so after they have been fed. These chases persist for several days, and ultimately they end in a kill. By the time success is achieved the young will have been encouraged by their parents to take prey in the air. Instead of leaving the prey at the nest or on a perch, the parents drop it in flight. The young can catch the prey within a fortnight of leaving the nest. The adult may later initiate a chase which ends in its releasing the prey for the young to grab.

Inexperience means that the young, despite being biologically programmed to hunt, may still not be good at finding food at first and must rely on parental contributions for a period. In the case of woodland-nesting species it is difficult to assess for how long this dependence lasts. **Ospreys**, however, are confined by their choice of food to open water and thus can be more easily watched. They are dependent on their parents for at least ten days after fledging. Where there are several nests in proximity, the young may fly from one to another to beg and apparently receive food from birds other than their own parents.

Richard Meinertzhagen watched a pair of Ospreys in Sweden apparently trying to lure the juvenile from the nest by flying past it with a fish, which they then repeatedly dropped in the water in order to encourage the young to plunge after them.

NESTS THAT FAIL

Not every pair that becomes established successfully rears young. Some **Golden Eagles** may not breed at all for a year. This is presumably a form of population control. Eagles are long-lived birds: in captivity they have survived into their forties, and the oldest ringed wild bird was over 25. With a twenty-year life span and more than fifteen years of sexual maturity, there is no pressing need for Golden Eagles to breed every year.

Some young and more inexperienced raptors will pair, but not successfully rear young, because they fail to build an adequate nest. Others may lay eggs, but inadvertently break them. Where populations are expanding, as with **Red Kites** in Wales and **Ospreys** in Scotland, new nests on the edge of the old range may fail in their first year, probably because the pair is inexperienced.

It is not unusual for raptors to lay infertile eggs. In some clutches all the eggs may be infertile, in which case the parent will incubate for so long that it is not possible for a replacement clutch to be laid that season. In others only some eggs may be infertile, which will not prevent the fertile egg or eggs from hatching.

Failure of the food supply is one obvious reason for deaths of chicks. Although the strategy of asynchronous hatching does allow survival of the elder chicks if food becomes short, in severe cases all the young may die.

Loss of eggs or young to predators is another reason for failure of a nest. Mammalian predators, such as squirrels or martens, and other raptors and owls may prey on eggs or young. The ground-nesting harriers are particularly vulnerable to the opportunism of ground predators and Crows when the female leaves the nest to receive food from the male. A quick-eyed Carrion Crow or Red Fox needs very little time in which to steal an egg or chick from the nest. At Minsmere in Suffolk, the reserve managers were faced with an interesting dilemma when a Bittern, nesting near a **Marsh Harrier** in a reedmarsh, developed a taste for young harriers and demolished the whole brood.

Before captive-breeding of **Peregrines** became possible, eyasses (nestlings) were taken from the nest by people who wanted them for falconry. This is no longer a serious problem in the British Isles, but it may still be in other parts of the Western Palearctic for other large falcons as well as for Peregrines.

On the Cape Verde Islands **Ospreys** have shown a marked decline because their eggs and young are taken for food, and there are some records of islanders in the Mediterranean taking the eggs of **Eleonora's Falcons** for food.

The curious desire to collect eggs seems to be a peculiarly British trait. This has been a particular problem for British raptors because of the attractive markings of the eggs and, certainly in the first half of the century, their rarity. Ironically that rarity probably owed something to the attentions of egg-collectors, and it was certainly these trophy-hunters who put the *coup de grâce* to some species, such as the **Osprey**, which had ceased to breed in the British Isles by the end of the second decade of the century and was subjected to raids by collectors when it returned forty years later.

The campaign to protect this vulnerable species from egg-collectors resulted in 24-hour watches that began to reveal previously unknown data about the behaviour at the nest of Ospreys. Now that sophisticated equipment is available, even more is being found out about the reasons for failure of raptor nests. In Wales, **Red Kites'** nests are watched with the aid of video cameras and image intensifiers, so that the reasons for nest failures (other than human intervention) are becoming clearer. When they are analysed, these tapes may reveal surprising information.

Some species of raptor have reputations for being very vulnerable to disturbance at the nest. Too much disturbance at the wrong time may cause the parents to desert the nest. This fact was reputed to be

Although Peregrines have lived for more than fifteen years in the wild, they rarely exceed ten years and two-thirds die within their first year.

exploited by some shepherds and keepers who, wanting to discourage **Golden Eagles** from nesting, would sit beneath an eyrie for a whole day to prevent the adults from returning to the nest. Some species, and individuals of otherwise apparently sensitive species, will be very tolerant of human interference, but as a strict rule any responsible birdwatcher should avoid approaching too close to the nests of any bird species, particularly raptors.

GROWING UP

The larger raptors are long-lived, but their life expectancy is comparatively short until they have survived their first autumn and winter. For example, little more than 40 per cent of **Ospreys** will survive to the end of their first year, but the survival rate doubles in subsequent years. This is mainly due to the inexperience of the first-year birds, for whom finding food may be difficult and who are vulnerable on migration to predation, usually from the trigger-happy trophy-hunter. Over two-thirds of **White-tailed Eagles** may not survive the first year and over 90 per cent die before reaching sexual maturity.

Sexual maturity takes several years to reach among the larger raptors. For **Griffon Vultures** it is in the fourth or fifth year, as it is for **Imperial Eagles**, but **Black Vultures** must wait for as long as six years. On the other hand, smaller raptors such as **Sparrowhawk**, **Red-footed Falcon** and **Kestrel** breed at the end of their first year. These species lay larger clutches than the bigger birds of prey, further differences being shorter life expectancy and even lower annual death rates. Half the individuals in these species die each year. Unusually for a larger raptor, the **Black Kite** has a similarly even 50 per cent mortality rate.

Sparrowhawks and **Kestrels** rarely reach as much as ten years of age. Although one male Sparrowhawk reached twelve, seven is the average life of a ringed wild male of this species, while for females the average is ten and the record fifteen. **Peregrines**, **Hobbies** and **harriers** rarely exceed ten years.

Death for raptors can come in a number of ways. Starvation is common, particularly among young birds in bad weather. A prolonged heavy layer of snow will prevent **Buzzards** and **Kestrels** from finding small mammals, for example. Disease seems to be unusual, although it is often difficult to identify death from disease. Carrion-eaters, which might be vulnerable to botulism and similar 'food poisoning', appear to have immunity.

Even predators are preyed upon, and death for some raptors comes at the talons of other, larger raptors and owls. But perhaps the most significant of predators on raptors is human. Deliberate death comes through poisoned bait, trapping and shooting. Mostly the birds are killed because they compete for prey with man, but some Europeans shoot **Honey Buzzards** for food: the breasts are a delicacy. In Malta and Greece, trophy-hunters shoot migrating raptors in order to stuff and mount them as trophies.

Human destruction of raptors is sometimes accidental. Pollution has killed large numbers of birds of prey, especially in the 1950s and 1960s, when persistent organochlorine pesticides were extensively used. Hunting raptors are sometimes killed when, intent on their prey, they fly into motor vehicles; and there have been cases of **Sparrowhawks** flying into windows, either in pursuit of prey or because they were confused by the reflections in the window.

AGGRESSION

When a bird at the nest or on the ground is threatened, it tries to make itself appear as large as possible to intimidate its opponent. All raptors employ the same fundamental threat display. The bird fluffs up the feathers on its head and neck, and stretches its head forward or upward with its wings partly or wholly open in a heraldic spreadeagle posture. It may rest on its hocks with its talons spread forward, ready to strike.

THREAT DISPLAYS

If confined and unable to escape or unwilling to leave the nest, raptors will attack mammals, including human beings. By staring at a raptor a person can usually deter it from attacking, but this may not always work: female **Hen Harriers** are particularly aggressive when cornered.

Attack is usually in defence of the nest against potential predators or in defence of a territory against other members of the same species. **Goshawks** defend their nests fiercely against predators and will fly at people walking through the woods nearby; intruders who climb a nest-tree may be attacked directly. **Golden Eagles** will swoop at foxes that approach the nest.

Griffon Vultures can be aggressive to one another at a kill. The degree of aggression seems to be linked to the degree of hunger rather than to a stable pecking-order based on individual recognition. The hungriest vulture is the most aggressive. In effect this is the latest arrival at a kill. The hungry vulture lands some distance from the huddle over the carcase. With head stretched forward and wings at a stretch, it bounds towards the kill; other birds give way, allowing it to find a place at the carcase. The aggression usually lasts no longer than a few minutes, by which time another hungry bird will have arrived. Only when there are many vultures and very little food does a hierarchy develop. The disputes between vultures may seem violent, but the aggression is ritualized and does not last long. The bare skin on the neck of the aggressive bird reddens, and it fluffs the feathers of its mantle. Head protruding and wings in a drooping stretch, it stares at its rival and blinks its nictitating membrane. The aggressor may then perform a foot-showing display: with neck outstretched and wings 'spread-eagled', it slowly raises one foot to breast height with the toes spread. This may be repeated several times as the underside of each foot is exposed. This display can become a high-stepping threat-walk, like a slow-motion goose-stepping march.

Stretching the neck is a feature of aggressive behaviour in flight. The **Short-toed Eagle** flies directly at intruders of the same species, its neck stretched out and wings forward calling loudly and repeatedly.

Sparrowhawks are fierce in defence of nesting areas. Nesting females are particularly aggressive towards rivals: there are usually more hens than cocks. Rivals are chased immediately if they are found near the nest-site, and overflying birds may be subjected to the slow-flighting display in which the territory-owner flies slowly back and forth above the trees on very slow, deep wing-beats. This may develop into the undulating flight. The hawk suddenly closes its wings for a distance of 5–10 m, then it momentarily spreads its wings and tail and swings upwards before closing its wings and dropping again.

While-tailed Eagles are fierce in defence of their nesting territory. Here a pair of eagles rises to meet an intruder.

Raptors will attempt to distract potential predators from the nest. Nesting **Peregrines** will drive away any bird that ventures near, and they will attack an intruder some distance from the actual nest-site in order to persuade the intruder that the nest is where the attack takes place. In the strictest sense these attempts are not distraction displays, because the expression usually describes behaviour in which a bird feigns injury to draw a predator away from the nest, eggs or young. The male **Osprey** will try to draw a predator away from the nest by suddenly faltering in flight and dangling a fish or, if it has none, dangling its legs; it makes a disyllabic call, repeated three times. As well as deploying this behaviour to distract eagles and gulls, it will also use it to distract other Ospreys.

Short-toed Eagles react aggressively to any other which intrudes into their territory. With necks outstretched, this pair drives off a young bird.

Short-toed Eagles have been seen to fall from the nest to the ground and walk away dragging a wing as if it were broken. The reputation of **Peregrines** for fierceness has been increased by incidents in which they have attacked people and dogs. In the 1920s in Devon, a woman saw a Peregrine attacking what she thought was one of her chickens: when she went to save it the Peregrine attacked her, tearing her apron and sinking its claws into her dress; it was killed. The 'chicken' was, in fact, a Kestrel. Both birds were subsequently stuffed and mounted.

Other raptors are discouraged by nesting Bonelli's Eagles. This one is attacking a Booted Eagle that has come too close to its nest-site.

Another pre-war incident in the West Country involved two Peregrines fighting on the ground in Dorset. A man walking a golden labrador and a fox terrier went to investigate. One bird flapped off with the labrador in pursuit; the other, a female, grabbed the fox terrier by the nose, pinning him to the ground. The dog was a fighter with other dogs, but the falcon's attack baffled him. He was released by his owner, who prised open the bird's talons. After pausing with wings half-open and feathers around the head erect, the female Peregrine flew off.

These are exceptional incidents; it is usually other birds that bear the brunt of the Peregrine's aggression. Those breeding at Gibraltar attack other raptors on their northward spring migration. The pair nesting on the east side of the Rock have attacked migrant raptors over the sea, and the victims, if struck, fall into the water. Short-toed Eagles are the most frequent victims, but Booted Eagles, Black Kites, Griffon Vultures and Sparrowhawks have also been attacked in this way. These raptors are also mobbed by Herring Gulls and local ornithologist E.F.J. Garcia has suggested that this mobbing confuses the raptors and makes them vulnerable to the attacks by Peregrines.

REACTIONS OF OTHER BIRDS

In the relationship between predators and prey the predator is not always dominant. The prey may take concerted retaliatory action. While the defence of the prey will sometimes be to lie still and remain unnoticed, it will also give an alarm call to attract other birds to mob the predator. The calls warning of predators are usually short, repetitive notes and remarkably similar among different species.

The Jay has a soft hawk-alarm call, described by Derek Goodwin as a 'very soft, sad alarm-call', which it gives while freezing and crouching as it watches the raptor. The pure tone of such a call makes it difficult to locate, so other Jays are warned of the danger, but the predator is not able to pinpoint the source of the call. It has been claimed that the Jay, which is an expert mimic, uses different calls to warn of different predators. If this were the case, the Jay would appear to be using onomatopoeia to give warning of a particular species of predator. Since imitating cats, dogs, squirrels, **Buzzards** or **Kestrels** is certainly not beyond a Jay's capability, the possibility should not be discounted.

When they are mobbing Tawny Owls, Jays will mimic an owl. The owl calls, both hoots and screeches, are usually made by Jays that are in the background, not the active mobbers. It is possible that by repeating the owl's call the mimics are fixing the calls in their own minds as part of the identification process, in a similar way to small children repeating the noises of a domestic animal to establish its identity. Possibly the older birds are the mimics, determined to give the young aural as well as visual identification features. One function of mobbing is thought to be imprinting on young birds the features of a predator at close quarters.

Among many birds there appears to be an innate ability to recognize raptors as potential predators. I have heard domestic geese giving alarm calls apparently in response to a passing **Kestrel**, which could do them no harm but which had a distinctly falconiform flight silhouette. In addition to the instinctive ability to recognize predators, mobbing may add skill in predator recognition. The mobbing calls of passerines differ from the hawk-alarm calls; they contain a mixture of high-frequency notes with good directionality. The calling birds' aim is to attract as many of their own and other species as they can. Presumably, the mobbed bird may become so irritated by the attentions of the small birds that it will be driven away. The hue-and-cry, as well as attracting other prey species may attract other predators, such as a larger raptor that might take the one being mobbed.

Small birds tend to keep out of reach of the raptor, but will fly up to it, scolding and flicking wings and tails in a gesture that it is easy to anthropomorphize as taunting.

In the case of ground-nesting species or species with nidifugous young on the ground, mobbing is probably no more than an attempt to drive away the raptor. In Suffolk, a pair of Shelducks was watched for over an hour and a quarter as it harassed a male **Marsh Harrier**; it was June, and presumably there were young Shelducks in the vicinity. At one point the ducks climbed together above the harrier, diving in unison and forcing the raptor to drop several metres as it had to slip to avoid them.

Attacks on predators in defence of the nest can be fatal to the predator. Two adult Carrion Crows and an immature were seen to attack a female **Kestrel** among the tops of tall trees. The observer, Bryan Sage, did not see the crows kill the Kestrel, but it dropped to the ground and died, with its neck broken.

Small birds in flocks may attack raptors in flight. Starlings will fly at a **Sparrowhawk**, worrying and confusing it. Swallows and martins will harry Hobbies. When I have seen prey species mobbing their predators in flight, the raptor has been in direct rather than hunting flight. Perhaps they recognize the raptor's full crop or some other feature that suggests to them that the predator is not a threat.

Bolder birds may attack raptors as pirates. Kites and Kestrels carrying prey will be fiercely attacked by Crows and Ravens trying

Ravens will attack any potential predator, however large, that enters their territory. This pair attacks an immature Golden Eagle.

Flocks of small birds such as Starlings will mob Sparrowhawks to harry and confuse them and thus deter them from attacking.

to make them drop their catch. I have seen two Carrion Crows and two young Grey Herons harrying an **Osprey** that had caught a fish. The Osprey flew with the fish to a large tree: the herons followed it into the tree, making it take to the air and then pursued it again; the crows waited until the Osprey perched before moving. If the Osprey had dropped the fish, the crows would have had the advantage over the herons in that they were stationary and could take off in which-ever was the best direction. The herons, which were already air-borne, would have had to change direction to grab the fish. To a fish-eating heron, an Osprey is a competitor. To an omnivorous crow an Osprey with a fish is an opportunity for theft of food.

MOVEMENT

Fundamentally, the reason for raptors to move from their breeding areas is to find food. There are four types of movement: dispersal from breeding areas, local movement, nomadism and migration.

DISPERSAL

Once the young can fly and catch their own food they leave the area of the nest, as there is unlikely to be enough food to sustain parents and offspring through the winter. How far and in which direction the young of non-migratory species have to travel varies.

The British **Sparrowhawks** studied by Ian Newton were breeding 1 km to 265 km from the site at which they were reared. The distance travelled will depend on the ease with which each bird finds an area that will sustain it. Since Newton found no cases of offspring mating with a parent or a sibling in subsequent years, post-breeding

Unlike many Red Kites in mainland Europe, Welsh kites do not migrate, but they do travel in search of food in winter.

At roughly four-year intervals, populations of lemmings explode. The extra food results in an increase in numbers of Rough-legged Buzzards, which are found in the following winters far beyond their normal range.

dispersal would appear to have the function of mixing birds from different localities.. There is no fixed, regular pattern: the young birds will move away as individuals in any direction.

LOCAL MOVEMENT

Local movement in search of food occurs when there are shortages in a particular locality. For example, moorland-nesting **Kestrels** may move from high ground to low ground in winter, when snow makes it difficult to hunt small rodents and small birds may already have moved. The **Red Kites** in Wales are largely non-migratory, but they may move from the wooded hills where they breed to refuse tips with is a surer supply of food. In Germany the kite population used to migrate south in winter, but in the last few decades there has been a rise in the numbers staying throughout the winter. The probable cause is the increase in refuse tips, which has already accounted for increases in and changes in the behaviour of gulls. If this proves the

Large numbers of Red Kites pass through Organbidexxa in the French Pyrenees on their autumn migration to southern Spain and North Africa.

case with Red Kites, it is ironic that this species, now rare in Britain, should have been common in English towns in the sixteenth and seventeenth centuries, when it fed on the rubbish that accumulated in the streets. As people became more tidy and their guns more accurate, the numbers of kites dropped dramatically.

NOMADISM

Alongside local movements there is nomadism, in which birds move from one area to another, staying wherever food is plentiful. This occurs among species in areas where food supplies may change radically as a result of sporadic rainfall. Nomadism occurs in desert species, and in the Western Palearctic has been noted among **Sooty Falcons**.

A variation in a species' movements from year to year may occur when there is a crash in the numbers of prey. Such a crash creates an irruption, when large numbers of a raptor species will move beyond its normal range. The **Rough-legged Buzzard** is an irruptive species. It preys on small rodents, mainly lemmings and voles. These irruptions occur in approximately four-year cycles. When rodent populations are healthy, the raptors lay more eggs and successfully raise more young. A sudden drop in rodent numbers makes the Rough-legged Buzzards move in search of food. Thus, large numbers are seen to the south and west of the species' normal range.

MIGRATION

The most dramatic and well-known movement is migration, which can be defined as an annual movement of birds from one area to another and back. Many elements of it remain a mystery, but our knowledge has increased rapidly with ringing schemes, radar, radio telemetry and the observations of thousands of birdwatchers. The value of the work of raptor-watchers is shown in a paper on raptor migration at Eilat by Hadoram Shirihai and David Christie, in which they detail the discrepancy of tens of thousands between the numbers of migrating **Lesser Spotted Eagles** in Israel and the published information on breeding numbers.

Raptors such as the snake-eating Short-toed Eagle – seen here performing a sky-dance – which specialize in cold-blooded prey, are migrants that winter south of the Sahara.

TABLE 1 HABITATS OF ACCIPITRIFORMES AND PANDIONIFORMES

	Tundra	Taiga	Deciduous woodland	Moorland and mountain	Steppe	Semi-arid woodland and moorland	Desert and semi-scrub	Wetlands and coasts	Towns
Honey Buzzard *Pernis apivorus*			M						
Black-winged Kite *Elanus caeruleus*				R	R				
Black Kite *Milvus migrans*			M		M	M		M	M
Red Kite *M. milvus*			p		p	p			
White-tailed Eagle *Haliaeetus albicilla*	M	R	R	R		R		R	
Bearded Vulture *Gypaetus barbatus*				R					
Egyptian Vulture *Neophron percnopterus*					M	M	M		M
Griffon Vulture *Gyps fulvus*						R	R		
Lappet-faced Vulture *Torgos tracheliotus*							R		
Black Vulture *Aegypius monachus*					R	R	R		
Short-toed Eagle *Circaetus gallicus*					M	M	M		
Marsh Harrier *Circus aeruginosus*								p	
Hen Harrier *C. cyaneus*		(M)		p	p			p	
Pallid Harrier *C. macrourus*					M				
Montagu's Harrier *C. pygargus*				M	M	M			
Dark Chanting Goshawk *Melierax metabates*						R[1]			
Goshawk *Accipiter gentilis*		(p)	R			R			
Sparrowhawk *A. nisus*		(M)	p			p			(p)

114

	Tundra	Taiga	Deciduous woodland	Moorland and mountain	Steppe	Semi-arid woodland and moorland	Desert and semi-scrub	Wetlands and coasts	Towns
Levant Sparrowhawk *A. brevipes*						M			
Buzzard *Buteo buteo*			R			p			
race *B. vulpinus*		M		M					
Long-legged Buzzard *B. rufinus*						p			
Rough-legged Buzzard *B. lagopus*	M								
Lesser Spotted Eagle *Aquila pomarina*									
Spotted Eagle *A. clanga*		(M)						M	
Tawny Eagle *A. rapax belisarius*							R[2]		
Steppe Eagle *A. (rapax) nipalensis*									
Imperial Eagle *A. heliaca*						M			
Golden Eagle *A. chrysaetos*		M		M		M			
Booted Eagle *Hieraaetus pennatus*						M			
Bonelli's Eagle *H. fasciatus*						R			
Osprey *Pandion haliaetus*								m	

KEY

M migrant
m mainly migrant
p partially migrant
R resident

Symbols in parentheses refer to isolated or discrete minor populations.

[1] Normally a bird of the sub-Saharan savanna, there is a small discrete population in Morocco.
[2] The small population in Morocco is found in semi-arid mountains and desert edge; sub-Saharan birds are found in savanna.

TABLE 2
HABITATS OF
FALCONS

	Tundra	Taiga	Deciduous woodland	Moorland and mountain	Steppe	Semi-arid woodland and moorland	Desert and semi-scrub	Wetlands and coasts	Towns
Lesser Kestrel *Falco naumanni*				M	M			M	
Kestrel *F. tinnunculus*				p	p	p	p		M
Red-footed Falcon *F. vespertinus*			M	M	M				
Merlin *F. columbarius*		M		M	M				
Hobby *F. subbuteo*			M		M				
Eleonora's Falcon *F. eleonorae*							M		
Sooty Falcon *F. concolor*						M	M		
Lanner *F. biarmicus*				R	R	R		R	
Saker *F. cherrug*				M	M	p			
Gyrfalcon *F. rusticolus*	M	R							
Peregrine *F. peregrinus*	M	M		p	p	R	R	p	p
Barbary Falcon *F. peregrinoides*					p	p			

KEY

M migrant
m mainly migrant
p partially migrant
R resident

Raptors that migrate have adapted to do so in order to exploit food sources in different geographical areas. At the top of the food chain, they are dependent for their food on the behaviour of their prey. Cold-blooded animals hibernate during winter, or in the case of some insects spend their winters in a passive state, as eggs, larvae or pupae. Reptile-eaters and insect-eaters must therefore either change their diet or to go to a place where reptiles and insects are available, which is why they migrate to sub-Saharan Africa. Many raptors feed on small birds which in turn eat insects, and they, too, have to migrate to find food, but they may not necessarily travel so far south: Merlins from northern Europe winter in southern Europe.

It is not, however, so easy to categorize every species as a migrant or not. In addition to the local movements described above, some populations of each species within the Western Palearctic are migrants. Migration appears to be linked to the habitat which the population occupies (See Tables 1 and 2). For example, the eastern race of the Buzzard, known as the **Steppe Buzzard**, breeds from eastern Europe to Siberia and is wholly migratory: the bulk of the population moves south to Africa, from Ethiopia down to South Africa; the remainder winter in southern Europe and the Middle East.

Peregrines that breed in the tundra move south, leapfrogging other European populations and continuing to South Africa. On a smaller scale, those British **Kestrels** which migrate also leapfrog, with northern Kestrels reaching Spain and the south of France while southern ones cross the English Channel to northern France.

Different wintering areas of the same species are not always a sign of leapfrogging. For example, some Scandinavian **Ospreys** winter in South Africa, 4000 km further south than others wintering in West Africa. This does not appear to be leapfrogging, because the winter destination seems to vary with individual birds rather than with different breeding populations, but no one has yet found a satisfactory explanation for the apparently pointless extra 4000-km journey.

Travelling from the Russian tundra to winter in South Africa, a **Peregrine** makes a journey of about 14,000 km in autumn and returns a similar distance the following spring. **Red-footed Falcons** breeding on the Russian steppes travel some 30,000 km to their winter quarters in south-west Africa and back.

OVERLEAF *Some species of migratory raptors cross the Mediterranean Sea on a broad front. Migration takes place over several weeks and each species tends to migrate over a particular period. It is, therefore, very unlikely that the species illustrated would all be seen at the same time. They are, from the top left: Peregrine, Eleonora's Falcon, Osprey, Marsh Harrier, Honey Buzzard, Lesser Kestrel, Montagu's Harrier, Kestrel and Hobby*

Eleonora's and **Sooty Falcons** delay their breeding season so they have young in the nest during the autumn migration of passerines. Both of these also winter in Madagascar, but they occupy different parts of the island: Eleonora's in the east, and the more numerous Sooty in the north and south-west. A few Eleonora's Falcons seem to winter elsewhere: about three hundred were present throughout one December–March rainy season in southern Tanzania, and a similar number has been reported to remain in the Aegean Sea. This is just one example of the need for more information about the wintering behaviour of raptors. There are still many gaps in our knowledge.

Most **Lesser Kestrels**, whose main food is insects and small reptiles, are sub-Saharan migrants, but not all go south for the winter. Some remain in southern Spain, North Africa and the borders of Turkey and Syria. This resident population consists of adults and may be as much as a quarter of the breeding population.

There are differences in wintering behaviour between birds of different ages. The adult **White-tailed Eagles** breeding in northern Russia stay in their breeding areas throughout the winter, but the immatures move south. The latter may not return to their breeding grounds for several years, until they reach sexual maturity. Second-year **Honey Buzzards** often remain in Africa throughout the summer and succeeding winter. Similarly, **Ospreys** do not return until their third summer, but these birds, which do not usually breed, move north more slowly than the adults and arrive later.

Not all populations of Ospreys are migrant. In Corsica, the breeding adults are resident and the non-breeding adults and young of the year migrate southwards. The timing of migration also varies between adult and young birds.

Sparrowhawks in Sweden move south when songbirds begin to migrate, which suggests that the stimulus to move may be the migration of their songbird prey. Songbirds leave their breeding grounds before their food has become scarce, because they need the food to build up their energy reserves for their migration. Among those species that are partial migrants, the individuals that migrate must do so because they are finding it increasingly difficult to find food.

Broad-winged migrants migrate by rising on one thermal and gliding down to the next and repeating the procedure. Since there are no thermals at sea, these raptors have to cross to Asia and Africa at the narrowest points, such as the Straits of Gibraltar and the Bosporus. From the top, left to right: Egyptian Vulture, Lesser Spotted Eagle, Red Kite, Buzzard, Steppe Eagle, Black Kite, Spotted Eagle, Booted Eagle, Honey Buzzard, Imperial Eagle and Sparrowhawk. Raptor migration takes place over several weeks and some species travel earlier than others. Therefore this selection is unlikely to be seen in the sky together.

The stimulus to migrate is not always food. Because of their experience, adults are more efficient hunters than their offspring and might be expected to stay longer on the breeding grounds as food becomes scarcer, but this is not always the case. There appears to be a pattern of migrating Sparrowhawks through Heligoland, whereby the sequence of birds moving southwards during October is juvenile males, juvenile females, adult males and adult females, with a reverse pattern in spring. With **Ospreys**, however, the adults leave their breeding areas two weeks earlier than their offspring, and adult **Black Kites** leave up to three weeks earlier. Adults travel faster than their young and so arrive several weeks earlier than the latter.

Raptors migrate in two ways: on a broad front, crossing seas, and on a narrow front, crossing seas at the narrowest points only.

Broad-front migrants are those with comparatively high wing-loading and which are able to make the journey principally with direct flapping flight. Harriers, Ospreys and falcons are broad front-migrants. Ospreys are capable of crossing the Mediterranean and the Sahara; they fly across the desert in one 2000-km journey, which takes between forty and 66 hours.

It is rather less easy to see the migration of broad-front migrants. Except for the colonial species, such as **Lesser Kestrel**, and **Red-footed** and **Eleonora's Falcons**, they migrate singly. They are most likely to be seen when they pause to feed or rest on their journeys.

The broad-winged raptors tend not to feed while on migration, because there is insufficient food along the routes that they follow to sustain such large numbers. They must rely, therefore, on thermals on which to soar as they migrate. Soaring up on the rising spiral of warm air in a thermal, the raptor then glides down to the next thermal and repeats the process. Thermals are created as the earth warms up in the morning. Wind also helps birds to slope-soar, in which rising air is created by the wind meeting a cliff or a hillside. There are advantages for soaring birds in migrating in flocks, as the chances of thermals being discovered are increased by the many pairs of eyes. Flocks of migrating raptors are often of mixed species, but **Honey Buzzards** and **Black Kites** tend not to mix with other species. **Booted Eagles** do not usually flock. Honey Buzzards have relatively long wings and will migrate on a broad front as well as in flocks, using thermals. Thus, at Falsterbo on the southern tip of Sweden, the Honey Buzzards with their lower wing-loading are able to set out to cross to Denmark sooner than **Buzzards**, which, with their higher wing-loading, have to wait for perfect soaring conditions.

The thermals, which raptors use for soaring, occur over land masses and not over the sea, so the raptors avoid the sea, crossing at the narrowest points: the Strait of Gibraltar, Falsterbo in southern Sweden, the Bosporus, and, in lesser numbers, the Dardanelles and the Strait of Messina. There are four other major raptor-migration points: Borçka and Iskenderun-Belen in Turkey, Suez, and Kfar Kasem and Eilat in Israel. Of these places, where soaring birds pass through valleys, Eilat is the region's best raptor-watching point in spring.

Raptor-watching at Eilat has become very sophisticated since counts began in 1977. Motor vehicles in radio contact with each other are used to ensure that the same birds are not counted twice and that the 100-km front across which the birds travel is adequately covered. Radar, motorized gliders and meteorological information are used to produce as accurate information as possible. Nevertheless, there are wide variations in numbers recorded. In autumn, when radar has been used to count birds across the breadth of Israel, there is an annual variation of 8 per cent in raptors counted, but in spring, when coverage has been confined to three or four points in the Eilat mountains and when weather can make the birds deviate from their usual course, the numbers may deviate by 46 per cent.

Studies from a motorized glider enabled the Israeli observers to calculate accurately the altitudes and speeds of flocks. The height at which the migrating raptors travelled varied among species and with time of day, but the average height band was between 344 and 1123 m. The actual speed at which they progress from point to point on the ground varies with climatic conditions and the altitude of the flock; in stable conditions the speed may be no more than 13 kph, while in unstable conditions it reaches as much as 60 kph.

The distance covered was calculated as part of these studies, and for four species it seems that their route is lengthened by 57.2–91 per cent in order to minimize effort and conserve energy.

The study of raptor migration has developed considerably during the last thirty years, but much remains to be discovered, particularly about the eastern routes through the Western Palearctic. This is another area of study in which the amateur ornithologist can still make a considerable contribution.

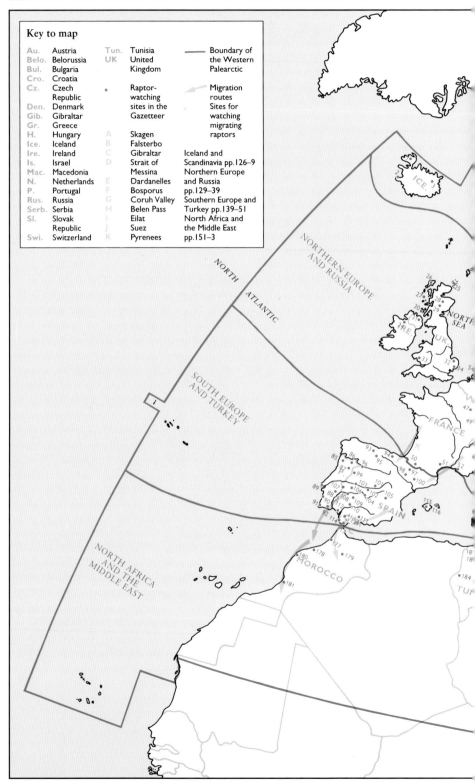

Key to map

Au.	Austria	Tun.	Tunisia
Belo.	Belorussia	UK	United
Bul.	Bulgaria		Kingdom
Cro.	Croatia		
Cz.	Czech	•	Raptor-
	Republic		watching
Den.	Denmark		sites in the
Gib.	Gibraltar		Gazetteer
Gr.	Greece		
H.	Hungary	A	Skagen
Ice.	Iceland	B	Falsterbo
Ire.	Ireland	C	Gibraltar
Is.	Israel	D	Strait of
Mac.	Macedonia		Messina
N.	Netherlands	E	Dardanelles
P.	Portugal	F	Bosporus
Rus.	Russia	G	Coruh Valley
Serb.	Serbia	H	Belen Pass
Sl.	Slovak	I	Eilat
	Republic	J	Suez
Swi.	Switzerland	K	Pyrenees

—— Boundary of the Western Palearctic

⟋ Migration routes

• Sites for watching migrating raptors

Iceland and Scandinavia pp.126–9
Northern Europe and Russia pp.129–39
Southern Europe and Turkey pp.139–51
North Africa and the Middle East pp.151–3

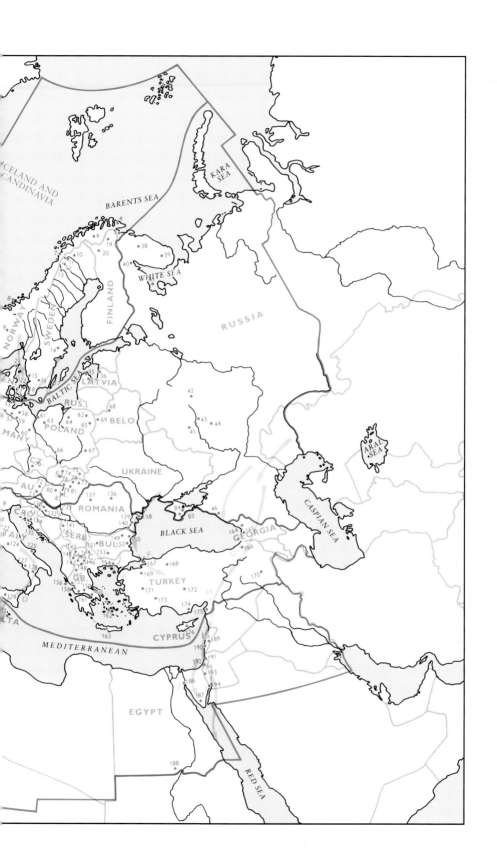

GAZETTEER

Raptors can be seen throughout the region and the nature of birds means that almost any species may turn up anywhere, but to stand a good chance of seeing some species it is necessary to travel. This gazetteer makes no claim to being comprehensive. It is arranged from north to south in four sections corresponding to those on the map on pages 124 and 125: Iceland and Scandinavia, Northern Europe and Russia, Southern Europe and Turkey, and North Africa and the Middle East. The number preceding each entry refers to its location on the map.

ICELAND AND SCANDINAVIA

Iceland

Basalt is the base-rock, and part of this large island is still volcanic. Lowlands are dwarf-shrub moorland, grassland and sedge-bog. Upland areas are often boggy, and above 600 m there is a high alpine zone of dwarf shrubs, herbs and mosses.

Absence of small rodents and reptiles means that raptors must rely on birds and blue hares as the major source of prey. With more than three hundred pairs of Gyrfalcons, the island is a stronghold the species. The population of thirty to forty pairs of White-tailed Eagles is increasing.

1 Haelavikurbjag and **Hornbjag** These remote seabird cliffs on the tip of the north-western peninsula are also sites for breeding Gyrfalcon and White-tailed Eagle.

2 Breidafjördhur Thousands of islands and rocky islets are contained in this huge shallow bay. 70 per cent of the country's White-tailed Eagle population breeds here: they are best seen from the Snaesfellsnes Peninsula on the southern shore.

3 Myvatn This shallow eutrophic lake is surrounded by bogs, small lakes and marshes. Birdwatchers will want to see the Barrow's Goldeneye, Harlequin Duck and divers breeding here, but it is also a good site for Gyrfalcon and Merlin.

Norway

Almost three-quarters of Norway is mountainous, and only 3 per cent of the land is under cultivation. In the north and above the tree-line the vegetation is arctic. To the south and west are woodlands, mainly of spruce and pine. The Norwegian population of one thousand pairs of White-tailed Eagles is the largest in Europe. The other two significant raptors are Golden Eagle with six to seven hundred pairs, and Gyrfalcon with two to five hundred pairs.

4 Tanamunningen Estuary with shallow water and sandbanks. White-tailed Eagle and Gyrfalcon in winter.

5 Øvre Pasvik Virgin forest near Finnish and Russian borders, with breeding Rough-legged Buzzard, White-tailed Eagle and Osprey.

6 Alta-Kautokeinoelva River valley with canyon, bogs and lakes. High density of breeding raptors: Rough-legged Buzzard (fifty pairs), Golden Eagle (three pairs), Merlin (thirty pairs), Gyrfalcon (five pairs), Kestrel (eleven pairs) and one pair each of Goshawk, Sparrowhawk and Peregrine.

7 Salstraumen Inlet and tidal river, with a wintering population of about 25 White-tailed Eagles which may grow to one hundred birds when food is abundant.

8 Smöla Archipelago White-tailed Eagles breed and more than fifty winter. Peregrine and Gyrfalcon also winter.

Europe's largest falcon, the Gyrfalcon, breeds in Iceland and northern Scandinavia. Sites where it is likely to be seen include Lake Myvatn in Iceland, the Hardangervidda in Norway and Finland's Pallas-Ounstunturi National Park.

9 Hardangervidda National Park Largest mountain plateau in Europe, with breeding Golden Eagle, Osprey, Gyrfalcon and Merlin.

Sweden

This large country is dominated in the north-west by mountains, with coastal lowlands around the Baltic. Throughout the country are lakes. Vegetation in the coastal fringe in the south-west is deciduous woodland and heath. Most of the south is dominated by pine and spruce forests with some oak and hazel. Much of the remainder of the country is covered by coniferous forest and peatbog. There is an alpine zone in the mountains to the north.

Although the range of raptor species is not wide, the estimated numbers are impressive. The White-tailed Eagle population fluctuates between 75 and one hundred pairs. Rough estimates put

Merlin hunting a Meadow Pipit. The five thousand pairs of Merlins breeding in Sweden is one of Europe's largest populations of this species.

Honey Buzzard at 8000 pairs, Hen Harrier at between one thousand and 2000, Osprey at over 2000 pairs, Merlin at 5000 and Gyrfalcon at less than one hundred.

10 Taavavuoma Marshes, streams, lakes and pools in a depression in a plateau in Lapland. White-tailed and Golden Eagles, Gyrfalcon and Peregrine breed.

11 Sjaunja Wetland wilderness, with forest and mountains in west. White-tailed and Golden Eagles and Gyrfalcon breed.

12 Lake Tjälmejaure Two valleys in mountains in northern Sweden. Hen Harrier, Rough-legged Buzzard, Golden Eagle, Osprey, Merlin, Gyrfalcon and possibly Peregrine breed.

13 Vindelfjällen Mountains Virgin spruce and birch forest with creeks and marshes. White-tailed (possibly) and Golden Eagles and Gyrfalcon breed.

14 River Dalälven Broad river with lagoons. About ten pairs of Ospreys nest.

15 Getterön Island joined by causeway to mainland. Raptors are seen on passage; White-tailed Eagle and Peregrine winter.

16 Lake Åsnen Large lake with many inlets and surrounded by coniferous forest. Probably northern Europe's densest breeding population of Ospreys, with about 45 pairs. Marsh Harrier and Hobby also nest.

17 Öland Long, narrow Baltic island close to Swedish mainland, with breeding Marsh and Montagu's Harriers and on passage Golden and White-tailed Eagles and Rough-legged Buzzard. Small numbers of both eagles winter.

18 Falsterbo Southernmost tip of Sweden where large numbers of raptors concentrate on passage. More than 20,000 Honey Buzzards and over 36,000 Buzzards have been recorded. Other migrants include Red Kite, Hen and Marsh Harriers, Osprey, Rough-legged Buzzard, Sparrowhawk, Hobby and Peregrine.

A female Hen Harrier quartering open moorland in search of small rodents. About six hundred pairs breed in Finland. Some breed in the vicinity of Lake Inari.

Finland

Much of central and southern Finland is low-lying, but the north is more hilly with deep river valleys and plateaux covered with tundra. There are over 60,000 lakes in Finland. Taiga, peatlands and reed-marsh are among the habitats in the southern and central parts.

The breeding raptors for which the country is important are Honey Buzzard (eight to nine hundred pairs), Hen Harrier (six hundred pairs), Osprey (nine hundred to one thousand pairs), Merlin (1600 pairs) and Gyrfalcon (20-25 pairs).

19 Lake Inari is a large lake (over 70 km by 30 km) surrounded by marsh and forest. Hen Harrier, Rough-legged Buzzard and Merlin breed.

20 Pallas-Ounastunturi National Park A mountain range near the borders with Norway and Sweden. Lower slopes forest-covered, the high tops tundra. Gyrfalcon breeds in vicinity of Konkama River.

Denmark

Although no part of Denmark is more than 175 m above sea-level, most of the countryside is gently rolling. Almost all the land is farmed, with a few remaining areas of oak and beech woodland, heath and coastal dunes. Some eight hundred pairs of Honey Buzzards breed, but the greatest raptor interest is largely in migrants moving to and from Scandinavia.

21 Rabjerg Mile Dunes and moorland at northernmost tip of Jutland near Skagen. Raptors on passage are, according to John Gooders, best seen from the hill of Flagbakken. Buzzard, Rough-legged Buzzard, Honey Buzzard, Hen Harrier, Red Kite, Sparrowhawk, Osprey and Hobby are all regularly seen. Other raptors recorded include White-tailed and Golden Eagles, and Red-footed Falcon.

22 North Zealand The northernmost point of the large island of Zealand is a popular viewing point for migrant raptors: Sparrowhawk, Buzzard, Rough-legged Buzzard and Honey Buzzard. Buzzard, Honey Buzzard and Sparrowhawk breed in beech woods.

23 Vestamager Three nature reserves near Copenhagen. Non-breeding raptors include White-tailed Eagle, Hen Harrier, Rough-legged Buzzard, Golden Eagle and Merlin.

NORTHERN EUROPE AND RUSSIA

Ireland

The lowlands of Ireland form a central plain surrounded by a perimeter of mountains. Peatbogs dominate the areas not farmed or under forest. Farmland is predominantly cattle pasture. Less than 1 per cent of the native deciduous woodland survived seventeenth-century clearance.

The ornithological importance of Ireland lies mainly in its seabird colonies and wintering wildfowl, but healthy populations of Hen Harrier, Merlin and Peregrine are probably internationally important. Breeding Hen Harrier and Merlin are found on the moorland and Peregrine on the sea-cliffs.

24 County Donegal Moors The blanket bog of the moors around Lough Derg, Brownhall, Lough Golagh and the Dunragh Loughs are a regular site for breeding Merlins.

United Kingdom

Varied habitats, almost all changed by land-use. Lowlands in the south and east are mainly arable; the uplands in west and north are farmed for livestock. Seabird colonies and moorland birds, which include Golden Eagle, Merlin and Hen Harrier, are of international importance. The Peregrine population of some thousand pairs is of European importance.

25 Orkney These islands are a stronghold for the Hen Harrier. West Mainland moors have 53 breeding pairs and seven pairs of Merlins while Orphir and Stenness Hills have 25 and two of each.

26 Isle of Lewis Peatlands with poor pasture and heather. Over fifteen pairs of Golden Eagles and twenty pairs of Merlins.

29 Abernethy Forest Caledonian pine forest, moorland, marsh and rivers. Breeding Osprey and Golden Eagle.

30 Islay Large island with peatbogs, sea-cliffs, saltmarsh, moorland and pasture. Breeding Golden Eagle, Peregrine and Merlin.

31 Rathlin Island Large island with peatbogs and cliffs: six pairs of Peregrines.

A Golden Eagle sweeps low over moorland heather to flush a hare. Golden Eagles breed in Scotland and can be seen in the Cairngorms, Rhum, Lewis and Islay.

27 Rhum Large island with rocky coast and mountainous interior. Three or four pairs of Golden Eagle breed. The island is the centre for a White-tailed Eagle reintroduction scheme.

28 Cairngorms Uplands with plateaux, scree, lochs, peatbogs and pine forest. Golden Eagle, Merlin and Peregrine breed.

32 North Norfolk Coast The low-lying coastline of Norfolk has several nature reserves. Marsh Harrier breeds and Hen Harrier winters. Rough-legged Buzzard, Peregrine, Merlin and Red-footed Falcon may be seen on migration.

33 Dinas and Gwenffrwd This reserve among the oak woods and sheepwalks is typical of the kite country of mid Wales. Red Kite, Peregrine, Buzzard, Merlin, Sparrowhawk and Kestrel may be seen.

34 Suffolk Coast The marshes along the Suffolk coast have breeding Marsh Harrier. The RSPB reserve at Minsmere is a certain site for this species, and Hen Harriers also winter there.

Latvia

Small, low-lying country on the eastern shore of the Baltic. Much of the country is farmed, but some bogs and lakes remain. Ornithologically the most interesting birds are associated with the wetlands, but there are also breeding raptors.

35 Slitere State Reserve Woodland, farmland and bogs at northern end of Kurzeme Peninsula. Kolka Cape is a

bottleneck for migrating raptors: 12,000 in spring include Honey Buzzard, White-tailed Eagle, 3500 Sparrowhawk, 8500 Buzzard, Golden Eagle and Osprey.

36 Ollu and Kodu-Kapzemes Bogs Open landscape with three large and several small lakes. Breeding Golden Eagle, Osprey and Merlin.

37 Lake Engure Freshwater lake with islands, separated from Gulf of Riga by a wooded strip of land Breeding waterbirds and Honey Buzzard, White-tailed Eagle, Marsh Harrier, Spotted Eagle and Merlin.

Russia

Broadly, the vegetational zones occur in three bands: steppe, taiga and tundra. In the steppe, the breeding raptors include Pallid Harrier, Long-legged Buzzard, Steppe

A Pallid Harrier hunts a Ground Squirrel on steppe-grassland. These species is common in suitable habitat in Russia, migrating to Africa and India for the winter.

and Imperial Eagles, Lesser Kestrel and Red-footed Falcon. In the taiga, harriers breed around the lakes and rivers. Populations of Gyrfalcon and Peregrine breed in the tundra. The mountains of the Caucasus have very important populations of raptors, including all four Vultures.

38 Imandra Lake In the western part of Kola Peninsula, within Arctic Circle. Breeding White-tailed Eagle and Osprey.

39 River Ponoy Middle reaches of Ponoy, with marshy taiga and lakes. White-tailed Eagle, Osprey and Gyrfalcon breed.

40 Kandalaksha Bay Large rocky bay with 860 islands. White-tailed Eagle and Osprey breed.

41 Onega Bay Offshore islands in White Sea. White-tailed Eagle and Peregrine breed.

42 Oka Biosphere Reserve in south-eastern part of Meshchera lowlands, with rivers, coniferous and deciduous forest, bogs and open water. Black Kite, White-tailed Eagle and Osprey breed. Golden Eagle, Saker and Peregrine occur on passage.

43 Galichya Gora Forest-steppe, meadows and open water, with breeding Pallid Harrier and Black Kite.

44 Khoper Drainage basin criss-crossed by channels with over four hundred lakes, and pine, oak, alder and poplar woods. Breeding Honey Buzzard, Black Kite, White-tailed, Short-toed, Lesser Spotted, Spotted, Imperial and Booted Eagles, Osprey, Red-footed Falcon and Hobby.

45 Les Na Vorskle Mid-Russian steppe with oak woodlands. Breeding Black Kite, Hobby and Saker.

46 Caucasus Biosphere Reserve Western part of Caucasus, with Bearded, Griffon and Black Vultures and Golden Eagle.

France

A quarter of France's land area is wooded, 5–6 per cent is garrigue, maquis or heathland, about 3 per cent is wetlands and about 30 per cent grassland. Two-thirds of the land is farmed.

France's raptor populations are quite important. In the woodlands, between 8000 and 12,000 pairs of Honey Buzzards, up to 8000 pairs of Black Kites and 2300-2900 Red Kites breed. The population of Bearded Vulturea is between twenty and 25 pairs, and that of the Short-toed Eagle is over a thousand pairs. Between 136 and 239 pairs of Booted Eagles breed. Hen Harriers and Montagu's Harriers have populations in the region of 3000 pairs, and Marsh Harriers are between 700 and a thousand pairs.

47 Forêt d'Argonne A wooded ridge rises from the massive cereal prairies in the west. Honey Buzzard, Osprey, Goshawk, kites and Hobby are present all summer.

48 Lac de Der Chantecoq A lake with woodland and wet meadows, with breeding Honey Buzzard, Red and Black Kites, and Marsh Harrier. In winter, in addition to thousands of waterfowl and almost 2000 cranes, there are White-tailed Eagle, Hen Harrier and Peregrine. Osprey on passage.

49 Lac de la Forêt d'Orient Similar to Der Chantecoq and about 40 km to the south-west, with breeding Honey Buzzard and Kites. Red Kite, White-tailed Eagle, Hen Harrier and Peregrine winter. On passage Honey Buzzard, Kites, Osprey and Peregrine.

50 Pyrenees The north-facing French Pyrenees are less warm than the the Spanish side (see page 141), but there are significant raptor populations and five particularly good sites are: **Forêt d'Iraty; Cirque de Lescu, Vallée d'Aspe** and **Forêt d'Issaux; Vallées d'Ossau, du Bitet** and de **Soussoueou; Vallées du Lis** and **de la Pique;** and **Cirque de Gavarnie.** Each of these has breeding Bearded and Egyptian Vultures, Golden Eagles and Peregrines. Well over a hundred pairs of Griffon Vultures breed and in the woods there are Red Kites and Goshawks. At **Organbidexxa** there is a heavy passage of raptors, with about 10,000 Honey Buzzards (17,379 in 1981), up to 8700 Black Kites and 3800 Red Kites. Other species recorded include Egyptian Vulture, Short-toed Eagle, Marsh,

Montagu's and Hen Harriers, Booted Eagle, Osprey, Merlin and Peregrine.

51 Cévennes National Park The Grand Causses and the cliffs of the Gorge du Tarn make this a place worth visiting for its landscape alone or for its flowers, but it is also a wonderful place to watch raptors. Griffon Vultures are being reintroduced here and are present throughout the year,

Vulture, Kites, Honey Buzzard, Marsh and Montagu's Harriers, Short-toed Eagle and Lesser Kestrel breed. Golden and Bonelli's Eagles, Osprey, Red-footed Falcon, Hobby and Peregrine are all recorded, with occasional Eleonora's Falcons; Spotted Eagle in winter.

53 Corsica Four pairs of Bearded Vultures, four pairs of Golden Eagles, some

A Marsh Harrier drops into a reedbed in search of a vole. France has a population of up to a thousand pairs. They may also be seen on migration through the Pyrenees.

with Goshawk, Sparrowhawk, Buzzard, Red Kite, Peregrine and Kestrel. Summer visitors are Egyptian Vulture, Short-toed Eagle, Honey Buzzard and Hen Harrier.

52 Camargue Although this area is best known for its wetland birds, it can boast a remarkable line-up of raptors. Egyptian

twenty pairs of Peregrines and thirteen pairs of Ospreys breed. Scandiola reserve, where Osprey and Peregrine breed is best approached by sea. The local Sparrowhawk race is endemic to Corsica and Sardinia: it is smaller, darker and more densely barred than the main European race.

Netherlands

Much of the country is flat and reclaimed from the sea or from marshland. Two-thirds is farmed. Very large tidal mudflats still exist on the Waddenzee extending along the north German coast to Denmark. In the south there are a few remaining beech and oak woods and some surviving heathland.

It is for its breeding waterbirds and waders that the Netherlands is particularly significant, but among the raptors eight hundred pairs of Marsh Harriers and up to five hundred pairs of Honey Buzzards are noteworthy.

54 Flevoland Polder created when the IJsselmeer was drained. There are some woodlands with Goshawk and Honey Buzzard and wetlands with Marsh, Hen, and Montagu's Harriers. In winter there are Rough-legged Buzzard, Buzzard, Hen Harrier, Goshawk and White-tailed Eagle.

Germany

Most of lowland Germany is farmed, but much of the mountainous south is still forested. The Baltic shore is flat, with bays, peninsulas and small islands. There are large tracts of heathland and moorlands.

A young Montagu's Harrier. This species breeds at a number of sites in Germany, including the Galenbecker See and Unteres Odertal. In the Netherlands it breeds on the polders created by the draining of the IJsselmeer at Flevoland.

Germany has the largest central European populations of White-tailed Eagle and Osprey, with about 120 pairs of each. Its population of 4500 pairs of Red Kites is the largest of any country. Black Kite (eight hundred pairs) and Marsh Harrier (1500 pairs) have healthy populations.

55 Kiel Bay The low-lying shore of the Baltic has estuaries, coastal marsh and islets on which there are seabird colonies. It is also a good place to watch raptors on passage. There are breeding White-tailed Eagles,which also winter here. Osprey, Peregrine and Honey Buzzard on passage.

56 Lauenbürgische Seen A protected area of lakes, forest and heathland, with Honey Buzzard, Black and Red Kites, White-tailed Eagle and Marsh Harrier.

57 Teichgebiet Lewitz Low-lying marsh in the Elde valley with numerous carp-ponds. As well as breeding waterbirds, there are Black and Red Kites, Marsh Harrier and Osprey. Wintering White-tailed Eagle and Hen Harrier in small numbers.

58 Galenbecker See and **Putzarer See** Two shallow lakes in drained fenland, with breeding Kites, White-tailed Eagle, Marsh and Montagu's Harriers, Lesser Spotted Eagle and Osprey. Spring and autumn passage of Red Kite and Hen Harrier. A few Hen Harriers overwinter.

59 Ostufer Müritz, Grosser Schwerin and **Steinhorn** Nature reserves over a range of habitats around a large freshwater lake. Breeding Honey Buzzard, Red and Black Kites, White-tailed Eagle, Marsh Harrier and Osprey. Hen Harrier on spring passage.

60 Unteres Odertal: Polder bei Schwedt River and shipping canal with reedbeds and polders. Honey Buzzard, kites, White-tailed Eagle, three harriers and Osprey breed. Wintering White-tailed Eagle and Peregrine.

Poland

Only 9 per cent of Poland is above 300 m. There are many lakes, particularly in the north, and coastal lagoons on the Baltic coast. Over a quarter of the country is wooded, but mainly with young stands; pollution has affected many of the forests. Fragments of hornbeam, oak and linden forests remain in the north-east. Some natural conifers remain in the mountains of the south, but most have been planted.

The Polish population of over three hundred pairs of Red Kites is increasing. Other significant populations of raptors are Honey Buzzard (2500 pairs), White-tailed Eagle (one hundred to 120 pairs), Marsh Harrier (1500–2000 pairs), Montagu's Harrier (two to three hundred pairs), Lesser Spotted Eagle (about six hundred pairs) and Spotted Eagle (fifteen to thirty pairs).

61 Szczecin Bay Shallow estuary of River Odra. Breeding Marsh Harrier, feeding Red Kite and White-tailed Eagle. Wintering area for up to sixty White-tailed Eagles and about fifteen Red Kites as well as for wildfowl.

62 Biebrza Valley River valley with meadows, reed-marsh, sedge-fen and grassland. Breeding Honey Buzzard, White-tailed Eagle, three species of Harrier, and Spotted and Lesser Spotted Eagles.

63 Inski Landscape Park Forest with farmland and open water. Breeding Kites, White-tailed Eagle, Marsh Harrier, Lesser Spotted Eagle and Osprey.

64 Iława Forests Woods, lakes and marshes: breeding Honey Buzzard, White-tailed and Lesser Spotted Eagles, Black and Red Kites, Marsh Harrier and Osprey.

65 Białowieża Forest One of Europe's best surviving examples of primeval forest, with breeding Honey Buzzard, Short-toed, Booted and Lesser Spotted Eagles, and Montagu's Harrier.

66 Odra Valley Marshes, meadows, peatbogs and alder woods, with breeding Black and Red Kites, White-tailed Eagle and three species of harrier. Wintering White-tailed Eagle and Red Kite.

67 Lipa Fish-ponds Complex of fish-ponds and mixed forest. Breeding raptors include Honey Buzzard, Red Kite, White-tailed, Short-toed and Lesser Spotted Eagles, Marsh Harrier and Osprey.

Belorussia

Largely lowland with hills and lakes in east and north and high ground in the south.

68 Belovezhskaya Pushcha Virgin forest, meadows and ponds near Polish border. Breeding Honey Buzzard, Black and Red Kites, harriers, Lesser Spotted, Spotted and Booted Eagles and Peregrine.

69 Berezina Lowlands crossed by Berezina river: marshes, wet meadows and pine, birch and alder woodland. Breeding raptors include Spotted and Golden Eagles.

Czech Republic

The Czech Republic is mountainous along its northern and southern borders, with arable farmland and forest covering most of the rest of the country.

70 Třeboňsko Protected Landscape Area This basin has over five hundred fish-ponds with meadows, woods and rivers. There are several nature reserves here. Honey Buzzard, White-tailed Eagle, and Marsh, Hen and Montagu's Harriers all breed. Ospreys pass through on migration. White-tailed Eagles winter.

Switzerland

The Alps and the Jura dominate the topography of Switzerland and between them is the Mittelland plateau, which is a strip no more than 50 km wide from Lake Geneva to Lake Constance. The natural vegetation is deciduous forest, mainly beech and oak, but much is now farmland. As they progress higher in the mountains the hardwoods give way to spruce and pine.

Courting Hobbies chasing each other is a springtime sight above the riverine forest and meadows of the Marchauen-Marchegg WWF Reserve on the Austrian bank of the River March.

Displaying Golden Eagle. This species breed in the mountainous parts of Austria and in both the High and Low Tatra Mountains and the Vihorlat Mountains of the Slovak Republic.

Above the tree-line are alpine meadows and then boulder and rocks.

The farmland provides habitat for Black and Red Kites and Golden Eagles breed in the mountains.

71 Luzern Woods near the Sarner See have breeding Buzzard and Honey Buzzard, and Black and Red Kites. In the mountains to the south are Goshawk and Golden Eagle. Peregrine and Red Kite may be seen where the lake enters a gorge in the east.

Austria

Well over a third of Austria is forested, particularly in the mountains, and along the banks of the Danube and March are flooded riverine forests. The plains in the east are at the extreme western edge of the steppes that stretch across Eurasia.

As many as one hundred pairs of Golden Eagles breed here and other important breeding species are Black Kite, Marsh and Montagu's Harriers, Peregrine and Saker.

72 Marchauen-Marchegg WWF Reserve On the Austrian side of River March. Riverine forest, meadows and pools. Honey Buzzard, Black Kite, Montagu's and Marsh Harriers, Buzzard and Hobby breed, and both White-tailed and Lesser Spotted Eagles may also be seen in summer.

73 Neusiedler See Large eutrophic salt lake fringed by reed-marsh, famous for its wetland species, but worth visiting for its raptors which include Honey Buzzard, Black and Red Kites, at least 130 pairs of

Imperial Eagle soaring on large squarish wings. This species is not common in the Slovak Republic or Hungary, but it breeds among the wooded hills at several sites, including Borzony, Aggletek, Mátra and Zemplen. In autumn these Imperial Eagles move south to Bulgaria and Turkey.

Marsh Harriers, Lesser Spotted and Short-toed Eagles, Saker, Peregrine and Red-footed Falcon.

Slovak Republic

The mountain ranges and the limestone hills in the south have many breeding raptors: three hundred pairs of Lesser Spotted Eagles, 25 pairs of Imperial Eagles, fifty pairs of Golden Eagles, and fifty pairs of Sakers. Some six hundred pairs of Marsh Harriers breed in the country.

74 High Tatra Mountains National Park In Carpathians. Forest predominates, with beeches, pines, fir and spruce. Important for mammals and birds. Lesser Spotted and Golden Eagles, Goshawk and possibly Peregrine breed.

75 Vihorlat Mountains Mountain range with beech, maple, hornbeam and oak, with breeding Honey Buzzard, Black and Red Kites, Golden, Lesser Spotted, Short-toed, Booted and possibly Imperial Eagles, Saker and Peregrine.

76 Low Tatra Mountains National Park Beech, conifers and maple. Honey Buzzard, Lesser Spotted, Golden and (possibly) Spotted Eagles and Peregrine breed.

Hungary

The Great Hungarian Plain, crossed by the Danube and Tisza, with low mountains in the north. Over 70 per cent of the land is farmed, and 13 per cent forested. The natural steppe with oak woodland was felled three centuries ago and replaced with a farmed steppe-grassland. Breeding raptors are protected, with fifty pairs of Spotted Eagles, fifteen pairs of Imperial Eagles and up to fifty pairs of Peregrines. White-tailed Eagles breed in riverine forest along the Danube. Passage migrants that hunt on the steppes include Long-legged Buzzards, Pallid Harriers and Peregrines.

77 Zemplen Oak and beech woods among hills and volcanic outcrops, with breeding Honey Buzzard, Black Kite, and Short-toed, Lesser Spotted, Imperial and Booted Eagles, and Saker.

78 Aggtelek National Park Wide plateaux and karst, with woods of oak, beech, ash and hornbeam, rough grassland and heath. Breeding Honey Buzzard, Short-toed, Lesser Spotted and Imperial Eagles. Wintering Golden Eagle and Peregrine.

79 Borzony Wooded hills in north, with breeding Honey Buzzard, Black Kite, and Short-toed, Golden, Lesser Spotted and Imperial Eagles. In winter Peregrine and Golden Eagle.

80 Mátra Oak, beech and ash woods, with breeding Honey Buzzard, and Short-toed, Lesser Spotted and Imperial Eagles.

81 Hortobàgy National Park Steppe with salt lakes, fishponds, reed-marsh and woods. Four hundred pairs of Red-footed Falcons, Saker and Marsh and Montagu's Harriers breed. Passage migrants include Short-toed Eagle, Long-legged Buzzard and Saker. Up to 35 White-tailed Eagles winter.

82 Ocsa Mainly peatbogs, with damp alder woodland, meadows and open water. Raptors include breeding Honey Buzzard, Marsh and Montagu's Harriers, and Saker. Hen Harrier in winter.

Ukraine

Largely covered by steppe-grassland, farmed for grain. Breeding Pallid Harrier, Long-legged Buzzard, Steppe and Imperial Eagles, Lesser Kestrel and Red-footed Falcon.

83 Karadag Forest, meadows and coast, with breeding Honey Buzzard, Imperial Eagle, Saker and Peregrine.

84 Crimean Game Reserve Huge reserve in Crimean Mountains with oak-pine-beech forest, rivers and meadows. Breeding White-tailed Eagle, Egyptian, Griffon and Black Vultures and Short-toed Eagle.

SOUTHERN EUROPE AND TURKEY

Portugal

On the south-west of the Iberian peninsula, Portugal is a hilly country with low-lying land around the coast and in broad, fertile river valleys. The mountainous hinterland still retains some oak forest, heathland and pine woods, but much has become maquis and garrigue. The southern plains are grazed by sheep, arable or Mediterranean forest, particularly cork-oaks. Black-winged Kite (150 to two hundred pairs), Egyptian Vulture (forty to sixty pairs), Montagu's Harrier (one thousand to 1300 pairs), Griffon Vulture (one hundred to 150 pairs), and Lesser Kestrel (three to five hundred pairs) are the most important breeding raptors. Bonelli's Eagle also breeds.

85 Geres Mountain National Park Mountain complex with oak and pine forests, heathland, pasture and farmland. Breeding birds include Short-toed Eagle, Montagu's Harrier, Golden Eagle, Booted Eagle, Lesser Kestrel and Peregrine.

86 Montesinho Mountain National Park Oak and pine woodland, heath and upland pasture. Short-toed and Golden Eagles, Montagu's and possibly Hen Harriers and Peregrine breed.

87 Upper River Douro River valleys with steep schist and granite sides covered with sclerophyllous scrub and oak and juniper woodland. Breeding raptors include Black and Red Kites, Egyptian and Griffon Vultures (the majority of the Portuguese population, with over one hundred pairs), Short-toed, Golden, Bonelli's and Booted Eagles, Lesser Kestrel and Peregrine.

88 Monforte Plains Wheatfields and dry pasture, typical habitat of Black-winged Kite and Montagu's Harrier.

89 Sado Estuary Mudflats, sandflats, saltpans and fish-ponds, with breeding Marsh and Montagu's Harriers, and wintering Osprey.

90 Santo André Lagoon Coastal lagoon with reed-marsh, sand-dunes, pines and cork-oaks. Marsh Harrier and Black-winged Kite breed.

91 South-west coast Sea-cliffs, islets and stacks, tidal river, sand-dunes,

Spain

Apart from Switzerland, Spain has the highest average altitude in Europe. Most of the country is 300 m or more above sea-level, but particularly mountainous are the Pyrenees which separate Spain from France and extend westwards as the Cantabrian Mountains, the mountains of Léon, Sierras de Gredos and the Sierra Nevada. Lowlands occur around river valleys and estuaries. Climate varies from relatively wet coastal fringes and mountains in the north-west to

Spain is the European stronghold of the Booted Eagle with over five thousand pairs breeding. They winter south of the Sahara and may be seen migrating across the Strait of Gibraltar.

saltmarsh and scrub, with breeding Short-toed Eagle, Montagu's Harrier, Bonelli's Eagle and Portugal's only breeding Ospreys.

92 Guadiana River Valley Long, deep-sided river forming border with Spain. Breeding species include Black Kite, Egyptian Vulture, and Booted and Bonelli's Eagles.

the dry central areas. Habitat varies, too, with mountain slopes clothed in woodland, both pine and hardwood, wheat-growing in the central plateau, maquis and wetlands around estuaries.

Spain is of outstanding importance for raptors. Species of special interest are Black-winged Kite (over a hundred pairs),

A female Red Kite flies down to receive prey from her mate. Spain's population of at least five thousand pairs is the most important in Europe. Kites are widespread throughout the Iberian Peninsula, favouring areas with small woods or clumps of trees in which to nest and roost.

Black and Red Kites (Europe's most important population), Bearded Vulture (45 pairs), over a thousand pairs of Egyptian Vultures, four hundred pairs of Griffon Vultures and 365 pairs of Black Vultures, over one hundred pairs of Short-toed Eagles, Montagu's Harrier, Spanish Imperial Eagles (104 pairs), Golden Eagles (eight to nine hundred pairs), Booted Eagles (over 5000 pairs), Bonelli's Eagles (over seven hundred pairs), Lesser Kestrel (perhaps Europe's largest population) and Peregrine (1600 pairs).

93 Picos de Europa National Park Rugged massif with rocks, limestone cliffs, gorges and two small mountain lakes. Griffon Vulture, Short-toed and Golden Eagles and Peregrine breed.

94 Sobron Gorge Cliffs, woodland and scrub with almost one hundred pairs of Griffon Vulture breeding.

95 Ebro and Rudón Valleys Valleys of two rivers high in the limestone Cantabrian Mountains with cliffs, beech and oak woodland. Breeding Egyptian and Griffon Vultures, Golden Eagle and Peregrine.

96 Arribes del Duero Granite cliffs above the River Duero and its tributaries with oak woods, sclerophyllous scrub, grassland. Breeding Griffon and Egyptian Vultures, Short-toed, Golden and Bonelli's Eagles, and Peregrine.

97 Pyrenees The cliffs and forests of the High Pyrenees and their foothills are excellent for raptors. A selection of the best sites is given. The **Sierras de Leyre, Orba**

and **Illon** are limestone mountains with cliffs, gorges, scrub and woodland, where Bearded, Egyptian and Griffon Vultures (some seven hundred pairs), Golden Eagle and Peregrine breed. These and Booted Eagle breed in the Ordesa National Park, and **San Juan de La Peña** is a good site for Griffon and Bearded Vultures. At **Sierra de Guara**, a limestone massif, Honey Buzzard, Red Kite, several pairs of Bearded Vultures, at least ten pairs of Egyptian Vultures and at least two hundred pairs of Griffon Vultures, Short-toed and Golden Eagles, and Peregrine breed.

98 Sierra del Moncayo Isolated mountain with oak and pine on northern slopes. At least one hundred pairs of Griffon Vultures, five pairs of Golden Eagles and Honey Buzzard breed.

99 Sierra de Guadarrama Mountain range, with breeding Griffon and Black Vultures, and Spanish Imperial, Golden and Bonelli's Eagles.

100 Río Martin 40 km of cliffs along river, with breeding Egyptian and Griffon Vultures, and Golden and Bonelli's Eagles.

101 Montejo de la Vega Limestone canyon, with 108 pairs of Griffon Vultures, Egyptian Vulture, Golden Eagle and Peregrine.

102 Sierras de Gredos Woodland, scrub and alpine grassland. Breeding Honey Buzzard, Black and Red Kites, Griffon and Black Vultures (fifty pairs), and Spanish Imperial, Golden and Booted Eagles.

103 Valle del Tietar Steep-banked river and two reservoirs. Breeding Black-winged and Black Kites, and Short-toed, Spanish Imperial and Booted Eagles.

104 Cortados del Jarama The rivers Jarama and Manzanares, with chalk cliffs and patchy willow, ash and poplar. Some fifty pairs of Black Kites, forty of Lesser Kestrels and ten of Peregrines breed.

105 Alto Tajo 80-km limestone canyon along upper Tajo. Egyptian Vulture, at least one hundred pairs of Griffon Vultures, Bonelli's Eagle and Peregrine (at least twenty pairs) breed.

106 Monfragüe Hills with cliffs and gullies, scrub, cork-oak. 120 pairs of Black Vultures makes this an excellent area. Other breeding raptors include Black-winged, Black and Red Kites, Egyptian Vulture, Griffon Vulture (165 pairs), Short-toed, Spanish Imperial, Golden, Booted and Bonelli's Eagles, and Peregrine.

107 Sierra de San Pedro Mountainous area on Portuguese border. Black-winged and Black Kites, Egyptian and Black Vultures, and Spanish Imperial, Golden, Booted and Bonelli's Eagles.

108 Zorita-Madrigalejo Undulating country under cereals or sheep-grazing. Breeding Black-winged, Red and Black Kites, Short-toed Eagle, Montagu's Harrier, Booted Eagle and Lesser Kestrel.

109 Embalse de Puerto Peña Large reservoir on River Guadiana with scrub, plantations and farmland. Black-winged and Red Kites, Griffon Vulture, and Short-toed and Booted Eagle breed.

110 Mallorca A flat island with mountains in the north-west. Breeding species include Short-toed and Booted Eagles, Marsh Harrier, Osprey and Peregrine. Eleonora's Falcon also breeds, and Black Vulture breeds in the mountains in the north-west.

111 Menorca Menorca has some important raptor sites. The limestone cliffs of the north coast hold breeding Peregrine and Osprey and the small mountains in the centre of the island at least twenty pairs of Red Kites, ten pairs of Egyptian Vultures and twenty pairs of Booted Eagles.

112 Sierra Morena de Córdoba Low mountain with Mediterranean scrub, oak woods and olive groves, with 75 pairs of Griffon Vultures, at least 22 pairs of Black Vultures, and Golden and Bonelli's Eagles.

113 Sierras de Cazorla and Segura Mountain ranges with high cliffs, pine woods, oak woods, grasslands and scrub. Only Spanish breeding site for Bearded Vulture outside Pyrenees. Also breeding are Griffon Vulture, Golden and Bonelli's Eagles and Peregrine.

114 Coto Doñana National Park Major wetland in the marshes of the estuary of the Guadalquivir. Important breeding raptors include at least sixteen pairs of Spanish Imperial Eagles, Black and Red Kites, and Short-toed Eagle.

115 Ronda and surrounding hills Ronda is a picturesque town where Lesser Kestrel breeds, and in the surrounding countryside there are Egyptian and Griffon Vultures, Short-toed, Golden, Bonelli's and Booted Eagles, and Peregrine.

116 Tarifa Coast bordering Gibraltar is a good point from which to watch the passage of birds crossing the Strait of Gibraltar. At least 39,000 kites pass here, as well as Short-toed Eagle and Osprey.

Gibraltar

117 Gibraltar On the tip of the Iberian peninsula,Gibraltar is an important crossing point for raptors migrating to and from Africa. The 250,000 that cross the strait may, if the wind is right, overfly the rock. 100,000 Honey Buzzards, 60,000 Black Kites, 2000 Egyptian Vultures, 5000 Short-toed Eagles, 1500 Montagu's Harriers and 10,000 Booted Eagles cross.

Italy

The Italian peninsula has considerable climatic variation, from the cool temperate north to the warm south with its almost rainless summers, resulting in four major geographical and vegetational zones. The Alps in the north have mixed forests and meadows. In the north-east the Po Valley, Italy's largest lowland area, has deciduous forest and pasture. The Appennines still have large areas of forest, but much has been cleared for agriculture. The coastal area is maquis and garrigue. The 5000-km coastline is a mixture of dunes, lagoons and marshes and cliffs.

Despite the reputation of Italians as bird-killers, the country boasts important populations of Egyptian Vulture (thirty to

45 pairs), Lesser Kestrel, Eleonora's Falcon and Peregrine (up to five hundred pairs each), and Lanner (one hundred pairs).

118 Val Camonica Mountains with rivers, streams, woodland and farmland, with Honey Buzzard, Black Kite, Goshawk and Golden Eagle.

119 Piedmontese Nature Reserves Media Val d'Ossola and Monte Mottace Val Grande are nature reserves in Piedmontese mountains, with breeding Honey Buzzard, Short-toed and Golden Eagles and Black Kite.

120 Val Maira Woodland, farmland and inland cliffs where Honey Buzzard and Golden and Short-toed Eagles breed.

121 Appennine Nature Reserves Five reserves from Passo del Cerreto to San Marcello Pistoiese in Tuscany. Mountains with woods, streams and farmland. Breeding Honey Buzzard, Goshawk, Golden Eagle and Peregrine.

122 Valle del Farma Hilly wooded area in Tuscany, with Short-toed Eagle, Black Kite, Montagu's Harrier and Lanner.

123 Tuscan Archipelago Islands with maquis, garrigue and sea-cliffs. In addition to seabirds, there are between fifteen and twenty pairs of Peregrines. Passage migrants include Honey Buzzard, Booted and Bonelli's Eagles and Osprey.

124 Abruzzo Nature Reserves and National Park Mountains with mixed and deciduous woodland, with breeding Honey Buzzard, Golden Eagle, Red and Black Kites and Peregrine.

125 Promontorio del Gargano Nature reserve under threat, with deciduous woodland, sea-cliffs and farmland: Egyptian Vulture, Honey Buzzard, Black and Red Kites, Short-toed Eagle and Peregrine breed.

126 Sardinia This large mountainous island with marshes and saltpans has important breeding raptor populations. Egyptian and Griffon Vultures, Marsh Harrier, Goshawk, Golden and Bonelli's Eagles, Eleonora's Falcon and Peregrine all breed. The local race of Sparrowhawk is smaller and darker than the main European

This high-soaring Goshawk is displaying its pale undertail coverts. In Italy, Goshawks breed on the wooded mountain slopes of Val Camonica in the north, the Apennine Nature Reserves and among the woodlands of the Massicio del Monte Pollino in the far south as well as on the island of Sardinia.

race. Up to 180 pairs of Eleonora's Falcons breed on islands off the south of Sardinia.

127 Monte Cervati and **Monte Sacro** Streams, farmland and deciduous woodland. Breeding Black and Red Kites, Golden Eagle, Lanner and Peregrine.

128 Massiccio del Monte Pollino Deciduous woodland, farms and mixed woodland. Breeding Black and Red Kites, Goshawk, Golden Eagle, Peregrine and Lanner. Bearded Vulture occasionally seen.

129 Sicily This island has breeding Red and Black Kites, Egyptian Vulture, Golden and Bonelli's Eagles, Eleonora's Falcon, Lanner and Peregrine. The **Montagne delle Madonie** is a good raptor breeding site and

nearby **Monti Peloritani** and **Monte Ciccia** overlooking the **Strait of Messina** provide a bottleneck for passage Honey Buzzard (about 6000), Black Kite, Egyptian Vulture, Marsh Harrier, Golden and Booted Eagles, Red-footed Falcon and Hobby.

Croatia

Much of Croatia is lowland and the riverine forests of the Danube, Kupa, Sadra and Odra have one of the largest populations of White-tailed Eagle in central Europe. Lesser Spotted Eagle and Saker breed.

130 Turopolje Wet meadows between the Rivers Sadra and Odra threatened by a proposed nuclear power station. Breeding Black Kite and White-tailed and Lesser Spotted Eagles.

131 Pokupsi Depression From the Zumberak Mountains to the River Kupa is a natural depression in which are over 11,000 ha of damp broad-leaved woodland with swathes of semi-natural grassland, streams and fish-ponds. Breeding Honey Buzzard, Black Kite, White-tailed and Lesser Spotted Eagles and Peregrine.

132 Sava Wetlands Floodplain of the Sava, Louja and Strug with alluvial oak and poplar forests, marsh, meadow, pasture and fish-ponds. Breeding Honey Buzzard, Black Kite, White-tailed Eagle, Lesser Spotted Eagle and Saker.

133 Kopački Rit Danube floodplain with large willow, poplar and oak. Important for breeding herons and up to twenty pairs of White-tailed Eagles, fifty pairs of Black Kites, and four or five pairs of Sakers. White-tailed and Spotted Eagles overwinter.

134 Paklenica National Park High-sided river canyons with beech, pine, oak and hornbeam. Egyptian and Griffon Vultures, Short-toed, Golden and Bonelli's Eagles, Peregrine and Lanner breed.

135 Krka National Park Forest, lakes, rivers and sea-coast, with breeding Short-toed, Golden and Bonelli's Eagles, Lesser Kestrel, Lanner and Peregrine.

Romania

Mountains account for about one-third of the country, hills and plateaux another third and plains the remainder. In the mountains above 1600 m, the alpine vegetation consists of herbs with pines, juniper and willow. Much of the montane area has been cleared for pasture, but three zones can be seen, with spruce and pine at higher altitudes giving way to mixed woodland and beech in the lower zones. The plains are mainly farmland with oak woods, steppe-woodland and, in the south-east, steppe. Wetlands occur along the Danube, with a major marsh complex at the Danube Delta.

Important breeding raptors are Pallid Harrier, White-tailed Eagle, Levant Sparrowhawk, Lesser Spotted, Golden and Imperial Eagles, Lesser Kestrel and Saker.

136 Bicaz Gorge and Lake Rosu Deep gorge in Hasmas Mountains with natural lake. Spruce, beech and mixed wood cover slopes. Breeding Golden and Imperial Eagles.

137 Intrgalde and Rimeti Gorges Two narrow gorges through Trascau Mountains. Surrounding area has beech woods, oak woods, meadows and farmland. Breeding Honey Buzzard, and Short-toed, Lesser Spotted, Golden and Booted Eagles.

138 Danube Delta Complex of channels, reed-marsh and meres with spectacular array of birds. Raptors among the 160-odd breeding species include White-tailed Eagle, Marsh Harrier, Osprey, Saker and Red-footed Falcon.

139 Niculitel and Babadag Forest Wooded hills and grassland. Breeding Short-toed Eagle, Levant Sparrowhawk, Imperial and Booted Eagles, Lesser Kestrel and Saker. Lesser Spotted Eagle occurs on passage.

140 Canaraua Fetii Canyon with barren slopes, deciduous woodland and luxuriant herbs. Breeding species include Honey Buzzard, Egyptian Vulture, Short-toed Eagle, Levant Sparrowhawk, Long-legged Buzzard, and Imperial and Booted Eagles.

Serbia

Most of Serbia is mountainous or hilly and only towards the Danube valley in the north does it become lowland riverine forest.

141 Fruška Broadleaved woodland with clearings, orchards, vineyards and farmland. Breeding Honey Buzzard, Imperial and Booted Eagles and Saker. Spotted and Lesser Spotted Eagles may also breed.

142 Bosutška Forest Riverine oak forest along River Sava, with Black Kite, Marsh Harrier and White-tailed Eagle.

Macedonia

The mountains of Macedonia have breeding Golden and Booted Eagles with Short-toed and Imperial Eagles, Long-legged Buzzard and Lanner.

143 Sara Mountains High mountains with river gorges, cliffs and rocky hillsides. Breeding Honey Buzzard, Golden Eagle, Peregrine, and Bearded and Griffon Vultures.

144 River Bregalnica Valley with woodland and steppe. Breeding Egyptian Vulture, Short-toed, Imperial and Golden Eagles, Montagu's Harrier and Peregrine.

145 Korab Mountain Gorges, cliffs, woodland and pasture. Griffon Vulture, Short-toed, Lesser Spotted, Spotted, Golden and Booted Eagles, Lanner and Peregrine.

146 Demir Kapija Gorge Cliffs, woodland and scrub. Breeding Honey and Long-legged Buzzards, Levant Sparrowhawk, Egyptian and Griffon Vultures, Short-toed, Imperial, Golden and Booted Eagles, Lesser Kestrel, Black Kite, Lanner and Peregrine.

147 River Crna Gorge Gorge with cliff, scrub and oak and beech woods. Egyptian and Griffon Vultures, Short-toed, Golden, Booted and Bonelli's Eagles, Lesser Kestrel, Lanner and Peregrine breed. Bearded and Black Vultures and Imperial Eagle occur.

148 Kozuf Mountain Pasture, cliffs, rocky hillsides, coniferous and beech woods. Breeding Honey Buzzard, Bearded and

A Spotted Eagle chases a Coot. The most westerly breeding population of Spotted Eagles is found in eastern Poland. The main breeding area is the southern edge of the Russian taiga. Some winter in the Danube flood-plain in Croatia or Serbia. Others winter in Turkey.

Griffon Vultures, Lesser Spotted, Golden and Booted Eagles and Peregrine. Small flocks of Eleonora's Falcons in summer.

Bulgaria

Much of the lowland has been converted to agriculture, but a third of the country is still forested. In the mountains are forests of oak, beech and pine. There are wetlands along the Black Sea coast and the River Danube.

Bulgaria's raptor population is important in European terms, but information about the sizes of individual populations is scant.

149 Yatata Reservoir Disused reservoir with numbers of White Pelicans and storks on spring and autumn passage, as well as raptors including Honey Buzzard, Black Kite, Marsh, Hen and Montagu's Harriers, and Lesser Spotted and Booted Eagles.

150 Cape Kaliakra Coastal headland which forms a bottleneck for autumn passage of Honey Buzzard, Black Kite, three harriers, Levant Sparrowhawk, Long-legged Buzzard, and Lesser Spotted and Booted Eagles.

151 Stara Planina Nature Reserves Three nature reserves that lie along the limestone Stara Planina mountains. Ancient forests of beech and spruce with pasture and scrub. Breeding Honey and Long-legged Buzzards, Golden, Imperial and Short-toed Eagles, and Peregrine. Possibly also Griffon Vulture, Lesser Spotted Eagle, Booted Eagle and Saker.

152 Cape Emine Coastal headland which forms a bottleneck for Honey Buzzard, Black Kite, Short-toed Eagle, Marsh Harrier and Lesser Spotted Eagle, in addition to over 100,000 White Storks and about 10,000 White Pelicans.

153 Studen Kladenetz Nature Reserve Artificial lake in rocky gorge of River Arda. Honey Buzzard, Egyptian and Griffon Vultures, Short-toed Eagle, Levant Sparrowhawk, Long-legged Buzzard, and Lesser Spotted, Imperial, Golden and Booted Eagles all breed. Griffon and Black Vultures are seen in winter.

Greece

Greece has a long, rugged sea-coast with many islands in the surrounding Ionian, Aegean and Mediterranean seas. The mainland is mountainous, with lowlands in narrow coastal bands and river floodplains. Only 19 per cent is now forested: many islands have been stripped of trees. Greece has more than a thousand endemic plants, giving it the richest flora in the region.

While there are large waterbird populations, the country is as important for its raptors. The 35 pairs of Bearded Vultures are found mainly in Crete. There are up to 250 pairs of Egyptian Vultures and 450 of Griffon Vultures. The one thousand pairs of Levant Sparrowhawks are the largest population in Europe and the 2800 pairs of Eleonora's Falcons form the majority of the world's population. Other significant species are Golden Eagle (220 pairs), Lesser Spotted Eagle (eighty pairs), Long-legged Buzzard (sixty pairs) and Lanner (between thirty and fifty pairs). The Lesser Kestrel, of which an estimated 2000 pairs bred in 1981, has plummeted.

154 Evros Delta and Mountains On the border of Greece and Turkey, this is one of Europe's most important wetlands, although it has been damaged by bad land management. In addition to breeding and wintering waterfowl, there are raptors on passage and wintering Hen and Marsh Harriers and Spotted Eagles. To the north, in the **Avas Gorge** in the Evros Mountains, the 24 breeding raptor and owl species include Honey Buzzard, White-tailed, Golden, Imperial, Short-toed and Booted Eagles, Egyptian, Griffon and Black Vultures, Levant Sparrowhawk, Goshawk, Buzzard and Long-legged Buzzard.

155 Lake Prespa Two lakes on the border with Albania and Macedonia. Marsh Harrier and possibly White-tailed Eagle breed. In the surrounding area there are Short-tailed and Golden Eagles, Egyptian Vulture and Long-legged Buzzard among the raptors.

156 Corfu Popular holiday destination from which the birdwatcher can see a great deal. **Lake Antinioti** in the north, **Lake Korisson** in the south-west and the **Alikes** in the south are wetlands where Ospreys and Marsh Harriers may be seen on passage. Red-footed Falcon and Hobby are also passage migrants. In the mountains in the north are Short-toed and Golden Eagles.

157 Zalongos Mountains A small mountain to the north of the Gulf of Amvrakia, with breeding Griffon and Egyptian Vultures and Booted Eagles, and Levant Sparrowhawk and Bonelli's Eagle possibly breeding.

158 Gulf of Amvrakia Short-toed, Lesser Spotted and Booted Eagles and Marsh Harrier breed. Osprey occurs on passage, and wintering species include Spotted Eagle and Hen Harrier.

159 Delphi A very popular tourist site but worth visiting both for its archaeology and for the raptors, best seen from above the running track. Peregrine, Sparrowhawk, Kestrel, Golden Eagle, Griffon Vulture, and Short-toed Eagle may be seen here. The nearby Mount Parnassus is worth visiting for raptors, including Bearded Vulture.

160 Mount Iti A mountainous National Park with a grazed plateau, forested slopes and ravines. Honey Buzzard, Short-toed and Golden Eagles and Peregrine breed. Vultures feed in the park.

161 Mesolonghi and **Aetoliko Lagoons** Saltmarsh, sandbanks and mudflats created by the rivers Achelos and Evinos are interspersed with rocky hills. Raptors breed on cliffs of Mount Arakinthos. Short-toed and Lesser Spotted Eagles and Griffon Vultures breed. Black Vulture, Hen Harrier, Spotted and Imperial Eagles and Peregrine winter.

162 Aegean Islands The small islands of the Aegean provide breeding sites for Eleonora's Falcon and Peregrine. The larger islands, such as Lesbos and Samos, off the coast of Turkey, have breeding eagles.

163 Crete The mountains are among the best sites in Europe to see Bearded Vulture. Other breeding species are Griffon

Bearded Vultures drop bones and tortoises to break them open.

Vulture, Short-toed, Bonelli's and Golden Eagles, and Peregrine. Some two hundred pairs of Eleonora's Falcons breed on Dia and almost three hundred pairs on the Dionisiades islets. The western end of the island is a good site for passage harriers.

Georgia

Mountainous country east of the Black Sea, with the only lowland around the estuary of the River Rioni. The Caucasus have several important breeding birds of prey.

164 Pshkuski Broadleaved forest with meadows and water. Breeding Black Kite.

165 Lake Ritsa Spruce forest around lake in southern Caucasus. with meadows and gorges. Breeding Bearded, Griffon and Black Vultures and Golden Eagle.

Turkey

This large country is partly in Europe and partly in Asia. On the European side of the Sea of Marmara the oak forest has largely been replaced by steppe. On the southern shore and along the coast of the Black Sea some forests of beech, oak and spruce persist, but much of the land is cultivated. The Aegean region is largely maquis, while the Mediterranean region is dominated by the Toros Mountains with their wooded slopes. Anatolia is mountains and plateaux. Much of the forest has given way to steppe.

Turkey is important for raptors in two ways: as part of a major migration route, and as breeding ground for four species of vulture, Long-legged Buzzard, Imperial Eagle, Lesser Kestrel and Saker.

166 Coruh Valley In north-east Turkey, this is a point where migrating raptors converge. Over 100,000 Honey Buzzards, 205,000 Steppe Buzzards and smaller numbers of Egyptian and Long-legged Buzzards, Short-toed Eagle, Marsh, Hen and Pallid Harriers, Sparrowhawk, Levant Sparrowhawk, Goshawk, Lesser Spotted, Spotted, Steppe, Imperial, Golden White-tailed and Booted Eagles, Lesser Kestrel,

Kestrel, Red-footed Falcon, Hobby, Saker and Peregrine.

167 Bosporus The Çamliça hills, the Princes Islands and Sanyer are good sites for broad-winged migrants. Maximum numbers for a single migration period are: Honey Buzzard, 25,700; Black Kite, 2600; Short-toed Eagle, 2300; Egyptian Vulture, 550; Levant Sparrowhawk, 5300; Lesser Spotted Eagle, 18,800; and Booted Eagle, 520.

168 Soguksu National Park Forested hills and valleys with scrub. Important raptor breeding site, with four species of vulture, Short-toed and Booted Eagles, Long-legged Buzzard and Peregrine.

169 Uludağ National Park Mountain in Western Anatolia with maquis, mixed woodland, alpine meadows and beech woods. Goshawk, Lesser Spotted Short-toed and Golden Eagles, Bearded, Black and Egyptian Vultures, and Peregrine breed.

170 Nemrut Daği National Park Sparsely vegetated volcano with two small lakes in its crater with hot springs and reedbeds. Breeding raptors include Egyptian and Griffon Vultures, Montagu's Harrier, Golden and Booted Eagles and Lanner.

171 Lake Isikh Freshwater lake at source of River Menderes. White-tailed Eagle, Griffon Vulture, Marsh Harrier, Golden Eagle and Long-legged Buzzard probably breed, and wintering raptors include White-tailed Eagle, Bearded Vulture, Hen Harrier, Spotted and Golden Eagles, Lanner and Saker.

172 Aladağlar Large mountainous area and valleys with orchards and forests. Black Kite, Egyptian, Bearded and Griffon Vultures, Short-toed Eagle, Long-legged Buzzard, Golden and Booted Eagles and Saker.

173 Lake Eğridir Western Anatolian lake with locally breeding Marsh Harrier, Egyptian and Griffon Vultures, Long-legged Buzzard, and Short-toed and Golden Eagles.

174 Göksu Delta Shallow lagoons with reedbeds, saltmarsh and sand-dunes. Breeding Marsh Harrier and Lesser Kestrel, as well as waterbirds. Wintering birds

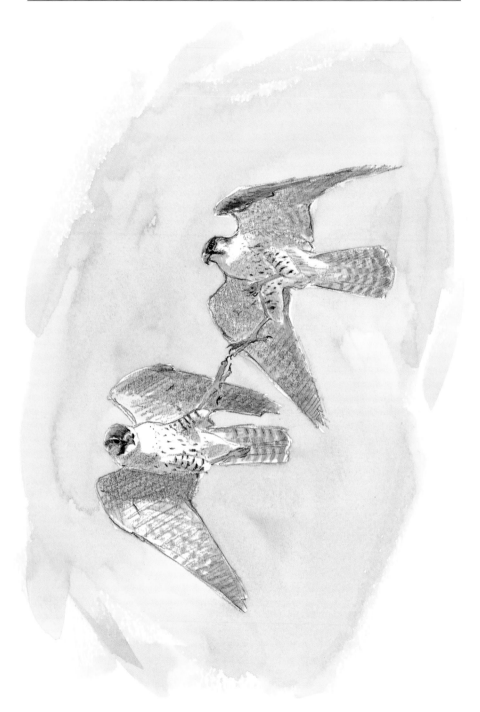

Displaying Lanners grapple talons. The population in Europe has plummeted, but the species still breeds in a few places in Turkey including the Nemrut Dagi National Park in the east.

include White-tailed Eagle, up to sixty Griffon Vultures, Marsh Harrier, Spotted Eagle and Peregrine.

175 Belen Pass A pass in the Amanus Mountains through which many raptors migrate in autumn. Species recorded include Honey Buzzard, Black Kite, Egyptian Vulture, Short-toed and Booted Eagles and Levant Sparrowhawk.

Cyprus

The island has been intensively cultivated, but forest still remains in the western parts of the Troödos Mountains and the Kyrenia range. Maquis remains in parts of the east and on coastal promontories. There are no perennial rivers, and the wetlands are shallow salt lakes on the Akrotiri peninsula and near Larnaca and man-made bodies of water on the southern side of the Troödos Mountains. Breeding raptors include about ten pairs of Griffon Vultures, one or two pairs of Imperial Eagles and perhaps a dozen pairs of Eleanora's Falcons.

176 Kensington Cliffs and **Akrotiri** Eleanora's Falcons and Griffon Vultures breed on Kensington Cliffs, and in spring and autumn Black Kite, Pallid Harrier, Osprey, Red-footed Falcon and Lesser Kestrel may be seen.

NORTH AFRICA AND THE MIDDLE EAST

Morocco

The western end of the Rif Mountains runs across the north of Morocco. Four mountain ranges run on a south-west–north-east axis across the country. The High Atlas reach over 4000 m. The southern slopes of the High and Middle Atlas are arid, while the northern slopes are wooded. The lower seaward slopes are Mediterranean maquis.

The only Eleanora's Falcons to breed outside the Mediterranean nest in two colonies off the Atlantic coast. Isolated populations of Dark Chanting Goshawk and Tawny Eagle breed in Morocco.

177 Merja Zerga A large shallow lagoon, excellent for waders in autumn, but also with passage raptors including Long-legged Buzzard, Osprey and Hobby. Black-winged Kites breed in the cork-oaks to the north and are present throughout the year.

178 Sidi Moussa The coast between **El Jadida** and **Cape Beddouza** has several good sites, including the marshes and salt-pans of Sidi Moussa and the cape itself. Barbary Falcon breeds, and passage migrants include Marsh and Montagu's Harriers, Long-legged Buzzard, Peregrine and Lanner.

179 High Atlas Bearded and Griffon Vultures, Long-legged Buzzard and Lanner breed.

180 Essaouira On the coast, with breeding Eleonora's Falcon. Passage raptors include Osprey.

181 Agadir is a centre from which birdwatchers can explore the surrounding countryside. In the vicinity of **Taroudannt**, Dark Chanting Goshawk and possibly Tawny Eagle breed. North of **Aulouz** in the High Atlas, there are Long-legged Buzzard, Bearded Vulture, Short-toed Eagle, Lanner and Barbary Falcon.

Tunisia

The highest ground in Tunisia is the Saharan Atlas, which covers most of the north of the country apart from the lowland coastal fringe. Cereals are grown at the eastern tip of the Atlas, on the south of which some forest remains. Olives are grown on the coast near Sfax. The rest of the country is steppe, merging into semi-desert and desert. The country is best known for its desert species and for its internationally important wetlands at Ichkeul and Kelbia with associated waterbirds.

182 Lake Ichkeul Ichkeul is renowned for its waterbirds, which include breeding

Marsh Harrier. Egyptian Vulture breeds in the hills nearby as do Lanner, Barbary Falcon and Peregrine. Eleonora's Falcon and Osprey may be seen on passage.

183 Lake Kelbia Another internationally important lake, with wintering Osprey, Bonelli's Eagle, Hen Harrier, Lanner and Peregrine.

184 Chott el Djerid Vast salt lake that may flood in winter. The surrounding desert has breeding Egyptian Vulture, Long-legged Buzzard, Lanner and Barbary Falcon.

Honey Buzzard, Osprey, Hobby and Eleonora's Falcon.

Egypt

Physically this large country is divided into three: Western Desert, the fertile Nile Valley and the mountainous desert in the east. Several species of raptor winter in the Nile delta, and the valley is a migration route. In the mountains, Bearded and Griffon Vultures, Sooty Falcons and

The Sooty Falcon is a desert species which is at the northernmost limit of its breeding range in Israel's Negev Desert, the Dead Sea and in Egypt's Sinai Desert.

Malta

These densely populated islands have a reputation for the illegal slaughter of passage raptors. Little natural woodland remains.

185 Buskett and Wied il-Luq A bird sanctuary that is a valuable roosting site for

Lanners breed. Egyptian Vultures breed in the Sinai Desert and to the west of the Nile. Black-winged Kites and Lanners breed in the Nile Valley.

186 Suez At the northern tip of the Gulf of Suez, this is a good place from which to watch the migration of raptors.

187 Sinai The Sinai has breeding desert species including Sooty Falcon, Lanner, and Egyptian and Griffon Vultures. Migrating raptors pass over the Sinai as they move north towards Eilat (see Israel). A good vantage point is **St Catherine's Monastery** in the southern Sinai.

188 Nile Valley Black-winged and Black Kites and Lanners breed along the Nile, and ancient sites such as Abu Simbel are good places for watching raptors.

Israel

For such a small country, Israel has a large number of species both breeding and passing through. The variety of habitats is the reason for the variety of breeding species, and its geographical position is the reason for the heavy passage through the country. Habitats range from snow-capped mountains to desert, and include forests, maquis, farmland, olive and fruit groves and wetlands.

On the southern edge of the Western Palearctic, it includes African and Asian species on the extremes of their breeding ranges: Sooty Falcon reaches the northern-most limit of its range on the shores of the Dead Sea, as does Lappet-faced Vulture in the Negev Desert. Israel can also boast spectacular passages of migrant raptors, including both falcons and broad-winged soaring birds. A total of 43 species of raptor has been recorded in Israel.

189 Golan Heights The mountains in the far north, where it snows regularly. There are woods, meadows and rocky scree. Griffon and Egyptian Vultures, Short-toed and Bonelli's Eagles, and Long-legged Buzzard breed.

190 Hula Ponds A major wetland nature reserve with large numbers of breeding waterbirds and wintering birds, including Spotted Eagle, Hen Harrier and Merlin. Raptors from surrounding area often roost in reserve.

191 Jericho Lesser Kestrel can be seen from the Monastery of the Temptation, and Bonelli's Eagle breeds in the Judaean Desert.

192 Ein Gedi and the **Dead Sea** The nature reserve at Ein Gedi on the edge of the Dead Sea is a resting place for migrating songbirds and a breeding site for Barbary Falcon. Griffon Vulture and Lanner breed locally. The cliffs to the west of the Dead Sea provide morning thermals for Lesser Spotted Eagles on spring migration. Sooty Falcons breeding near Sodom seem to feed mainly on bats.

193 Negev Desert Sooty Falcon, and Griffon Vulture breed in the Negev Desert, with Lappet-faced Vulture present but no longer breeding in the wild. At Nahal Habosar Nature Reserve on the edge of the desert, Imperial Eagle and Lanner may be seen. Long-legged Buzzard, Saker and Pallid Harrier are seen on migration.

194 Eilat More than a million raptors pass over Eilat in spring. Both spring and autumn passage can be spectacular. Passage migrants include, among many others, Short-toed and Steppe Eagles, Pallid Harrier, Honey, Long-legged and Steppe Buzzards, Osprey, Levant Sparrowhawk and a few Barbary Falcons.

BIBLIOGRAPHY

Alon, D., Leshem, Y., Dovrat, E., and Tsovel, A., 'Autumn migration of soaring birds: cross-Samaria and Northern Valleys' (1981-91), *Torgos* 20 (1992), 78

Birkhead, T.R., and Møller, A.P. *Sperm Competition in Birds: Evolutionary Causes and Consequences,* Acedemic Press, London, 1992.

Bond, R., 'Aggressive behaviour in Peregrine', *British Birds*, 39 (1946), 180

Brown, L.H., *British Birds of Prey*, Collins, London, 1976

Brown, L.H., and Amadon, D., *Eagles, Hawks and Falcons of the World* (two volumes), Country Life, London, 1968

Brown, R., Ferguson, J., Lawrence, M.J., and Lees, D., *Tracks and Signs of the Birds of Britain and Europe: An Identification Guide*, Helm, London, 1987

Craighead, J.J., and Craighead, F.C., *Hawks, Owls and Wildlife*, Harrisburg, 1956

Cramp, S., and Simmons, K.E.L., *The Birds of the Western Palearctic*, Volume II, OUP, Oxford, 1980

Dementiev, G.P., and Gladkov, N.A., *Ptitsy Sovietskogo Soyuza* 1 (1951)

Dubois, P.J., *Où Voir les Oiseaux en France*, Nathan, Paris, 1989

Errington, P., 'Predation and vertebrate populations', *Quarterly Review of Biology* 21 (1946), 144-77, 221-45

Garcia, E.F.J., 'Persecution of migrating raptors by peregrines at Gibralter', *British Birds* 71 (1978), 460

Glutz von Blotzheim, U.N., Bauer, K.M., and Bezzel, E., *Handbuch der Vögel Mitteleuropas*, Volume 4, Frankfurt am Main, 1971

Gooders, J., *Field Guide to the Birds of Britain and Europe*, Kingfisher, London, 1990

Gooders, J., *Where to Watch Birds in Britain and Europe*, Christopher Helm, London, 1988

Goodwin, D., *Crows of the World*, British Museum (Natural History), London, 1976

Grimmett, R.F.A., and Jones, T.A., *Important Bird Areas in Europe*, ICBP, Cambridge, 1989

Handrinos, G., and Demetropoulos, A., *Birds of Prey of Greece*, Efstathiadas Group, Athens, 1983

Hayman, P.J., and Burton, P., *The Birdlife of Britain*, Mitchell Beazley, London, 1976

Hill, M., *Bruno Liljefors: The Peerless Eye*, Allen, Kingston upon Hull, 1987

Hollom, P.A.D., Porter, R.F., Christensen, S., and Willis, I., *Birds of the Middle East and North Africa*, Poyser, Calton, 1988

Howard, R., and Moore, A., *Complete Checklist of the Birds of the World*, Academic Press, London, 1991

Jonsson, L., *Birds of Europe,* Christopher Helm, London 1992

Leshem, Y., 'Bonelli's Eagle', *Israel Land and Nature* 3 (1977), 9-15

Leshem, Y., 'Golden Eagles in our backyard', *Israel Land and Nature* 5 (1979), 70-75

Love, J.A., *The return of the Sea Eagle*, CUP, Cambridge, 1983

Lovegrove, R.L., *The Kite's Tale: the Story of the Red Kite in Wales*, RSPB, Sandy, 1990

Meinertzhagen, R., *Pirates and Predators*, Oliver and Boyd, Edinburgh, 1959

Newton, I., *Population Ecology of Raptors*, Poyser, Calton, 1979

Newton, I., *The Sparrowhawk*, Poyser, Calton, 1980

Paz, U., *The Birds of Israel*, Christopher Helm, London, 1987

Pearson, B., and Burton, R., *Birdscape*, HarperCollins, London, 1991

Poole, A.F., *Ospreys: A Natural and Unnatural History*, CUP, Cambridge, 1989

Porter, R.F., and Willis, I.R., 'The autumn migration of soaring birds at the Bosphorus', *Ibis* 110 (1968), 520–36

Porter, R.F., Willis, I., Christensen, S., and Nielsen, B.P., *Flight Identification of European Raptors*, Poyser, Calton, 1978

Ratcliffe, D., *The Peregrine*, Poyser, Calton, 1980

Rudebeck, G., 'The choice of prey and modes of hunting of predatory birds with special reference to their selective effect', *Oikos* 3 (1951), 200–31

Sage, B.L., 'Carrion Crows killing Kestrel', *British Birds* 55 (1962), 127

Shirihai, H., and Christie, D.A., 'Raptor migration at Eilat', *British Birds* 85 (1992), 141–86

Swenson, J.E., 'The relationship between prey species ecology and dive success in Ospreys', *Auk* 96 (1979), 408–13

Thiollay, J.M., *Oiseau* 37 (1967), 150–52

Tubbs, C.R., *The Buzzard*, David and Charles, Newton Abbot, 1974

Veysey, C.M., 'Shelducks diving at a Marsh Harrier', *British Birds* 53 (1960), 127

Walter, Hartmut, *Eleonora's Falcon: Adaptations to Prey and Habitat in a Social Raptor*, University of Chicago Press, Chicago, 1979

Walters Davies, P., and Davis, P.E., *British Birds* 66 (1973), 183–334 and 241-270

Watson, D., *The Hen Harrier*, Poyser, Calton, 1977

Willgohs, J.F., *The White-tailed Eagle* Haliaeetus albicilla albicilla *in Norway*, Bergen, Årbok for Universitet, 1961

SCIENTIFIC NAMES

All bird species mentioned in the text are listed below, with their scientific name, in systematic order.

Ostrich	*Struthio camelus*
Black-throated Diver	*Gavia arctica*
Little Grebe	*Tachybaptus ruficollis*
Fulmar	*Fulmarus glacialis*
White Pelican	*Pelecanus onocrotalus*
Bittern	*Botaurus stellaris*
Grey Heron	*Ardea cinerea*
White Stork	*Ciconia ciconia*
Whooper Swan	*Cygnus cygnus*
Shelduck	*Tadorna tadorna*
Eider	*Somateria mollissima*
Harlequin Duck	*Histronicus histronicus*
Barrow's Goldeneye	*Bucephala islandica*

ACCIPITRIFORMES
Accipitridae

Honey Buzzard	*Pernis apivorus*
Black-winged Kite	*Elanus caeruleus*
Black Kite	*Milvus migrans*
Red Kite	*M. milvus*
White-tailed Eagle	*Haliaeetus albicilla*
Bearded Vulture	*Gypaetus barbatus*
Egyptian Vulture	*Neophron percnopterus*
Lappet-faced Vulture	*Torgos tracheliotus*
Griffon Vulture	*Gyps fulvus*
Black Vulture	*Aegypius monachus*
Short-toed Eagle	*Circaetus gallicus*
Dark Chanting Goshawk	*Melierax metabates*
Marsh Harrier	*Circus aeruginosus*
Hen Harrier	*C. cyaneus*
Pallid Harrier	*C. macrourus*
Montagu's Harrier	*C. pygargus*
Goshawk	*Accipiter gentilis*
Sparrowhawk	*A. nisus*
Levant Sparrowhawk	*A. brevipes*
Buzzard	*Buteo buteo*
Long-legged Buzzard	*B. rufinus*
Rough-legged Buzzard	*B. lagopus*
Augur Buzzard	*B. rufofuscus*
Lesser Spotted Eagle	*Aquila pomarina*
Spotted Eagle	*A. clanga*
Tawny Eagle	*A. rapax*
Steppe Eagle	*A. (r.) nipalensis*
Imperial Eagle	*A. heliaca*
Golden Eagle	*A. chrysaetos*
Booted Eagle	*Hieraaetus pennatus*
Bonelli's Eagle	*H. fasciatus*

PANDIONIFORMES
Pandionidae

Osprey	*Pandion haliaetus*

FALCONIFORMES
Falconidae

Lesser Kestrel	*F. naumanni*
Kestrel	*F. tinnunculus*
Red-footed Falcon	*F. vespertinus*
Merlin	*F. columbarius*
Hobby	*F. subbuteo*
Eleonora's Falcon	*F. eleonorae*
Sooty Falcon	*F. concolor*
Lanner	*F. biarmicus*
Saker	*F. cherrug*
Gyrfalcon	*F. rusticolus*
Peregrine	*F. peregrinus*
Barbary Falcon	*F. peregrinoides*
Hazel Grouse	*Bonasa bonasia*
Quail	*Coturnix coturnix*
Pheasant	*Phasianus colchicus*
Coot	*Fulica atra*
Crane	*Grus grus*
Great Bustard	*Otis tarda*
Cream-coloured Courser	*Cursorius cursor*
Audouin's Gull	*Larus audounii*
Herring Gull	*L. argentatus*
Roseate Tern	*Sterna dougallii*
Arctic Tern	*S. paradisaea*
Feral Pigeon	*Columbia livia*
Budgerigar	*Melopsittacus undulatus*
Barn Owl	*Tyto alba*
Snowy Owl	*Nyctea scandiaca*
Tawny Owl	*Strix aluco*
Short-eared Owl	*Asio flammeus*
Alpine Swift	*Apus melba*
Skylark	*Alauda arvensis*
Swallow	*Hirundo rustica*
Meadow Pipit	*Anthus pratensis*
Wheatear	*Oenanthe oenanthe*
Blackbird	*Turdus merula*
Fieldfare	*T. pilaris*
Song Thrush	*T. philomelos*
Redwing	*T. iliacus*
Goldcrest	*Regulus regulus*
Jay	*Garrulus glandarius*
Magpie	*Pica pica*
Rook	*Corvus frugilegus*
Carrion Crow	*C. corone*
Raven	*C. corax*
Starling	*Sturnus vulgaris*
House Sparrow	*Passer domesticus*
Greenfinch	*Carduelis chloris*

INDEX

Page numbers in *italics* refer to illustrations